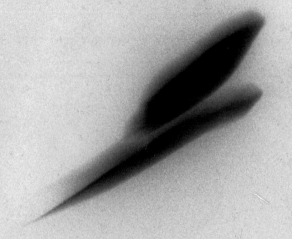

KILLER WHALES

JOHN STENERSEN · TIU SIMILÄ

© Tringa forlag, 2004
Design and repro: John Stenersen, Tringa as
Graphic production: Interface Media AS, Oslo
Printed by: PDC Tangen as, Aurskog
Translation: Richard Binns

ISBN 82-994577-3-4

Tringa Forlag
Dreyersgt. 1
N-8312 Henningsvær

e-mail: john@tringa.no
www.tringa.no

Contents

FOREWORDS

WHY WRITE a book about killer whales? What makes these animals so charismatic? The life history and behaviour of these animals is far too complex for a simple answer.

Killer whales are fascinating animals to study; the way populations have adapted to their environment, their skills as predators, the stable family groups, individualism, long life span and group specific vocal dialects are just a few examples of what makes these animals intriguing.

The fact that killer whales spend most of their time under water and events like mating, giving birth, hunting and playing are not easily observed makes them challenging to study.

Long-term studies of such animals becomes more than a job, it becomes a commitment. Following the life of known individuals for over a decade will give answers to many questions but at the same time raise a multitude of new ones.

Both of us have been introduced to killer whales by persons who know a lot about

these animals, and who had the enthusiasm and ability to share their knowledge. With this book we hope to be able to share with the readers a glimpse of the world of killer whales.

We want to thank all who have supported research on killer whales in Norway, in particular WWF whose long-term engagement has been invaluable.

The writing of this book has been a long process and several persons have come with valuable contributions. We would especially like to thank Geir Andersen for his insight in both writing and biology. Svein Spjelkavik has given us useful advice

in layout and Arne Kjeldstadli has given invaluable typographic advice.

Sigrund Krane and Mic Calvert have contributed with stories and pictures and George McCallum has given us access to his vast collection of killer whale pictures.

A warm thanks for all those good days in the field to Fernando Ugarte, Teo Leyssen, Stefan Hansen and Per Ole Lund. Fernando has also contributed to the contents of this book, the same has Børge Damsgård, Malene Juul Simon, Peter Corkeron, Sofie Van Parijs, Hans Wolkers and Anna Bisther.

And finally, loving thanks to our families – Cecilie, Aurora and Hauk, Anders, Jonatan and Kristian – for their patience.

Henningsvær / Bø i Vesterålen
25th. September 2004.

John Stenersen   •   Tiu Similä

THE KILLER WHALE

— KILLER WHALE POPULATIONS
AROUND THE WORLD

THE KILLER WHALE is the largest species in the dolphin family, and is easily recognised by the characteristic white markings on its predominantly black body. Adult males are distinguished by their tall, triangular dorsal fin, which stands straight up and can be more than one and a half metres high. Adult females have a smaller, more curved dorsal fin. Young animals have dorsal fins that resemble those of adult females, and their gender is often difficult to determine.

The size of killer whales varies somewhat from one area of ocean to another. Hunting statistics for Norwegian waters exist up to 1980 and show that full-grown males on average reach a body length of almost 7 metres, whereas females normally reach barely 6 metres. However, a few individuals have been found that greatly exceeded the average – males as long as 9.1 metres and females up to 7.9 metres. Pacific Ocean killer whales grow somewhat larger than those in our waters, whereas in the Antarctic there are populations that are made up of much smaller animals.

A new-born killer whale weighs around 180 kg and is just over 2 metres long. It is warm yellow to pale red on the light-coloured parts of its body, which are white on adults, and this colour gradually fades to white during the suckling period. Killer whales grow rapidly during the first ten years of their lives. Their growth rate then declines, but they do not become fully grown until they are 20-25 years old. Their average life span, calving intervals and other parameters vary from population to population. The average age of males is thought to be approximately 30 years, whereas females live ten years longer on average. However, far older individuals are known, males having reached an age of 50-60 years and females as much as 80 years.

The males do not become sexually mature before they are about 15 years old, and it is first at that age that the dorsal fin starts to grow quickly. The females normally have their first calf when they are around 15 years old and a typical female has five offspring during her reproductive period, which lasts until she is approximately 45 years old. Female killer whales continue to live and fill a social function in their families long after they cease to reproduce.

Gestation in killer whales lasts 16-17 months. Young can be born at any time of the year, but in Norwegian waters most births take place in late autumn.

Killer whales do not sleep in the same manner as terrestrial mammals. Breathing is not an automatic process in whales and requires that they always remain conscious. Research performed on dolphins in captivity indicates that they get rest by "disconnecting" half their brain at a time; half the brain rests while the other half controls their breathing. Their activity level is low during such resting periods. In the killer whale, it is typical for the animals in a group to undertake a series of regular dives during which they coordinate their movements and breathing rhythm. They may also rest on the surface for a few minutes at a time, lying motionless and breathing.

Marine mammals differ significantly from terrestrial mammals in the way oxygen is taken up by the body and internally transported. When a whale is lying on the surface, oxygen is taken up in an open system as in other mammals through air which is breathed into the lungs, transferred to the blood and conveyed out into the muscles along the arteries. However, they have larger amounts of haemoglobin in their blood and myoglobin in their muscles. Oxygen is stored in the muscles, to be used during diving. It seems that the lungs of deep-diving whales collapse during diving owing to the pressure. This also enables them to avoid nitrogen poisoning, which we know as decompression sickness or the bends.

The male NB-14 and a female from the NB-group. Note the differences in size and shape of the dorsal fin.

When humans draw in air and dive, most of the oxygen is stored in the blood, rather than in the muscles as in dolphins.

Killer whales spend most of their time in the uppermost part of the water body, and usually dive to depths of 30-40 metres. However, far deeper dives have been recorded, down to some 300 metres.

Killer whales have a large brain, which can weigh up to 5.5 kg in adult males. Relative to their body weight, this is about the same as in most primates and smaller than in humans.

To understand how killer whales live, we have to be able to imagine a weightless existence. Whereas gravity forces terrestrial mammals to live on the ground, whales can roam freely in the water, and their need for air is the only thing that regularly forces them to visit the surface. In such an environment, the need for the various senses will necessarily differ significantly from what we find in terrestrial mammals. In the toothed whales, smell and taste are generally poorly developed, but sight is good and the skin is sensitive to touch. Their hearing is acute and they are able to "see with their ears" through a highly developed echo-locating sense.

The eyes of a killer whale are located where they provide concurrently focused vision

The killer whale has a stereoscopic view downwards and forwards.

forwards and downwards, and clear images both above and below water. Norwegian killer whales are frequently curious about boats and often examine them more closely by swimming upside down beneath them, to get a stereoscopic view of them. Or they come to the surface and raise their heads above the water to take a closer look, this being referred to as a spy hop.

The killer whale has poorly developed colour vision, but its eyes are sensitive to contrasts. This is natural since colours become indistinguishable only a few metres beneath the surface and contrasts become all the more important in the underwater visual scene. Killer whales are also able to

swim upside down at a few metres depth to study the silhouette of a mammal or fish against the light surface.

The contrasting markings on killer whales probably enable the animals to coordinate their movements through visual contact. Their white ventral side and dark dorsal side make them difficult for potential prey to detect in the water; viewed from above or below the whale appears evenly coloured and inconspicuous.

Killer whales and other dolphins lack tear glands, but they have glands which bathe their eyes in a slimy liquid that does not dissolve in salt water. This reduces friction when swimming at high speed.

The skin is extremely sensitive when touched and physical contact between animals is an essential part of play and social behaviour in a killer whale community.

Little is known about the importance of taste, but killer whales have taste buds at the base of their tongue and some dolphin species are said to be able to taste different chemicals added to water. A possible advantage in having a sense of taste is that males can taste hormones expelled into the water via urine, which may tell them that a female is ready to mate. Perhaps killer whales can also "taste" the proximity of prey.

Hearing, however, is essential for killer whales, and differs considerably from our form of hearing. When we dive, it is almost impossible for us to determine the direction of sounds under water. Our ears are fastened to the skull, and the sound waves under water come from all directions approximately simultaneously, causing resonance in the skull. To avoid this, the ear in toothed whales is insulated from the skull.

The killer whale registers sounds through oil-filled canals in its lower jaw, which lead directly to the inner ear. The inner ear is formed of a group of tiny bones which are more compact than in other mammals. In contrast to the rest of the skeleton, the bones in the ear are fully developed from birth, thus demonstrating how important hearing is for the killer whale. At the rear margin of the eye, a small opening leads into the auditory canal, as in terrestrial mammals, but this is scarcely of any major biological importance.

Studies of killer whales in captivity show that they can hear over an extremely broad range of frequencies, from about 500 Hz to more than 100 kHz. By comparison, the human ear can register sounds on average between a couple of hundred Hz and 16 kHz. Killer whales hear extremely weak sounds, and can hear each other at a distance of at least 24 km. They use hearing both when communicating with others and when hunting. Sound also provides important information when they want to orientate themselves. They may register the sound of waves breaking on a coastline, moving ice, or water issuing from a river mouth.

The killer whale has a broad repertoire of sounds. These are created by pumping air back and forth between small air bags in the head. At the front of its forehead, the killer whale has an oil-filled "melon" – an acoustic lens - which concentrates and transmits sound waves forwards in the water. Sounds

The loud sounds from tail-splashing can be a part of the communication between killer whales..

produced when a killer whale jumps, or strikes its tail or fins against the water, may perhaps also be part of its communication.

The echo-locating sense, which we find in bats and toothed whales, acts roughly like an echo sounder in a boat. In whales, the sound pulses consist of a eries of high-frequency clicks that are transmitted out through the "melon". When they strike an object, the echo is reflected back, conveyed through the oil-filled canals in the lower jaw and registered in the brain.

With the help of echo location and hearing, killer whales form acoustic images of what they encounter under water. They seem to have a well-developed ability to remember these images, enabling them, for example, to recognise a prey the next time they record it, in the same way as we recognise something we have seen before.

Killer whales are well adapted to the three dimensional underwater world, where light is limited but sound carries a long way. Whereas we are almost totally dependent on sight, and construct most of our experiences on visual images, the killer whale mostly builds its experiences on acoustic images.

The killer whale is very well adapted to a life under water.

DISTRIBUTION

THE KILLER WHALE is a real cosmopolitan and probably the most widely distributed mammal in the world. It is found in every ocean and can be encountered from tropical waters as far as the ice edge round both poles. However most killer whales live in cold or temperate waters and close to coasts.

In common with most species of whales, little has been known about the size of the populations until recently. The most detailed study of killer whales has been carried out in British Columbia in Canada since the early 1970s. It was soon discovered that there were two different types of killer whales in these waters, one feeding on mammals and the other on fish. The latter seemed to be more stationary in the area and were called the "residents", while the former apparently only occurred on passage and were called the "transients". Subsequently, it has been discovered that the fish-feeding whales are not stationary; they are only regularly present in summer when there are salmon in the waters. These two groups differ genetically, and there is no exchange between them. Recently, it has been discovered that a third group of fish-feeding killer whales resides pelagically off the west coast of North America, and these whales have been called the "offshores".

In addition to these populations along the Pacific Ocean coast of North America, it is the killer whale populations along the

Most killer whales are found in cold waters. This is the Nc-group in the Vestfjord.

Norwegian coast, off Iceland, near the Crozet Islands in the Indian Ocean, off the coast of Patagonia in Argentina and around New Zealand that we have comparatively good knowledge of. Research is also being performed on populations near Gibraltar, off Kamchatka in north-eastern Russia, and in the waters around Australia, the Antarctic and the British Isles.

The members of the various populations are quite similar in appearance, but have a different vocal repertoire, social structure and behaviour, which are largely determined by their choice of prey and hunting strategy. The diet of killer whales is more varied than that of any other marine mammal; in different parts of the world, baleen whales, porpoises and dolphins, seals and sea lions, sea turtles, seabirds, squids and many different kinds of fish are on the menu. Where an energy rich prey species is readily available, the killer whales will specialise on that. Where such "offers" are not available, their diet seems to be more varied. The decisive factor is a kind of energy balance, where the whales, learning by experience, have found the diet which gives the highest nutritional profit with the least expenditure of energy. The presence of killer whales in a particular area over time, like off the coasts of British Columbia, Iceland and Norway, is determined by the availability of prey.

Norwegian killer whales live mainly on herring. The Norwegian spring-spawning herring undertake long, seasonal migrations and the whales follow the herring shoals. When the herring stock collapsed at the end of the 1960s, the herring changed their migration pattern. Whereas they had previously spent the winter in the open sea, they now began to migrate into fjords along the coast. Since 1987, the over-wintering area for Norwegian spring-spawning herring has been inner Vestfjord, Ofotfjord and Tysfjord, and most Norwegian killer whales congregate in this relatively small area each autumn and winter.

It is not accurate to speak of a Norwegian killer whale population, since there are strong indications that killer whales observed off the coast of Finnmark, in the Barents Sea, around Svalbard and in the North Sea belong to other populations. However, for the sake of simplicity, we refer to the herring-feeding population, on which all Norwegian killer whale research has been conducted, as the "Norwegian killer whales".

Previous page: The social structure varies between different killer whale populations.

KILLER WHALES AND PEOPLE

THE NAME "KILLER WHALE" implies that we have looked upon this animal as a bloodthirsty hunter. However, the name really derives from "whale killer" or "killer of whales", and alludes to the feeding habits of those killer whales which hunt large baleen whales.

Nowadays, it has become more common to use the name "orca", to avoid the tendentious "killer whale". This derives from the Latin name Orcinus orca of the animal, which has its origin in Linné's original description from 1758. He called the killer whale Delphinus orca, which means the "demon dolphin". The name "orca" is perhaps not much more appropriate nevertheless… The Norwegian name, "spekkhogger" (blubber cutter), also refers to the populations which live on baleen whales, and which Norwegian whalers got to know when they were hunting the large whales in Antarctic waters. However, along most parts of the Norwegian coast, where the killer whale is a relatively common sight, it is more usual to use the name "staurkval" (pole whale). This alludes to the large dorsal fin of the males which stands out of the water like a pole, and the name perhaps reflects a more relaxed view of these impressive creatures.

The first description we have of the killer whale is that of Pliny the Elder (AD 23-79), who described it in his Naturalis Historia as "an enormous mass of meat armed with terrible teeth". The conception of the killer whale as a dangerous animal has survived right up to our days. As recently as 1973, it was described in the American Navy Instructions to Divers as "extremely wild", and divers were warned that it "will attack people at the slightest opportunity".

However, the Indians on the west coast of North America have had an entirely different relationship to the killer whale. Totem practices and stories handed down by word of mouth show that the killer whale was held in high esteem by a number of the coastal tribes. Many of them caught various species of whales and dolphins, but the killer whale was apparently not hunted. On the contrary, it was highly respected, and many tribes had a taboo on injuring a killer whale; that would bring ill-luck. One story tells of a ritual where young men displayed their courage by canoeing unnoticed up to a group of resting killer whales to run over their backs before they had time to dive.

In the coastal parts of Norway where the killer whale is common, people do not appear to have feared them. It has always been known that the killer whale largely lives on herring. When it was periodically persecuted by people, this was because it was looked upon as a food competitor.

The killer whale has been little exposed to commercial hunting. The Japanese are the only whalers who have exploited the blubber and meat of killer whales for human consumption, and they hunted them on a limited scale until 1981. Russia hunted them commercially in Antarctic waters until 1981. In 1982, the International Whaling Commission banned the hunting of killer whales until their populations were better investigated. This ban has been respected throughout the world.

In Norway, killer whales formed only a minor proportion of the small whales that were traditionally hunted up to 1981. It had never been customary to eat their meat, which was mainly used as food on fur farms. However, fur farmers stopped purchasing whale meat at the beginning of the 1970s. Hence, killer whale hunting became unprofitable, and ceased for a time.

It was resumed in 1977, and intensified, owing to the collapse of the herring stock. The remnants of the over-fished Norwegian herring stock were concentrated in a few fjords for parts of the year, and were hunted by killer whales. The opinion was that the whales were a threat to the herring stock, and whale hunting was subsidised by the Government.

This form of "pest hunting" of killer whales was not confined to Norway. In British Columbia, Canada, in the 1960s and 1970s, it was not unusual to find individuals with shotgun wounds. In 1960, a high-calibre machine gun was set up at a river mouth on Vancouver Island to shoot the killer whales to protect the salmon stocks in the area. It was never fired because the whales changed their migration pattern and found other hunting grounds in the region.

Off Iceland, the fishermen received assistance from the American Navy to chase away killer whales in the 1950s. The aim was to scare them from the fishing grounds by shooting after them, mainly because they damaged fishing gear.

However, there are also stories that tell of a positive relationship to killer whales. In the 1800s, humpback whales were hunted off south-eastern Australia by men who rowed from land in small, easily-rowed boats to attack the whales with hand-held harpoons. This primitive manner of hunting lasted nearly a century and the hunters took close on one hundred whales a year. They ascribed their success to a group of some 30-40 killer whales!

These whales lived in the area throughout the Australian winter, feeding on seals and the occasional minke whale. However, as soon as the humpbacks arrived during their annual migration from the Antarctic to more temperate waters, the killer whales shifted their hunting behaviour. They attacked in groups and grasped the long flippers of the far larger humpbacks in their teeth. When they had surrounded a humpback, a signal was given from a watchtower on land, and the whalers jumped in their boats.

As killer whales often require a long time to kill a large baleen whale – assuming they manage it at all –the whalers just had to get out to the struggling creature as quickly as possible to harpoon it to death. The dead animal was then towed in to shallower water, and the killer whales followed. The harpooned whale was anchored and the whalers went away. The killer whales could then begin their feast, concentrating on the soft parts around the humpback's mouth, and its tongue.

The carcass sank, but floated up again after a day or so because of the gas that developed inside it, and the whalers were able to row out and take their prey. They thought the killer whales had shared their prey with them because they had cooperated in the pursuit. We have since learnt that killer whales which live on large baleen whales never eat the entire animal, but are satisfied with choice soft parts.

From the modern whaling era, too, in both the Antarctic Ocean and the Norwegian Sea, killer whales have been known to follow whaling boats and try to help themselves to dead and dying animals. However, they did not assist the whalers; on the contrary, they were regarded more as a pest.

In modern times, there has been considerable interest for keeping killer whales in aquariums and entertainment parks. This created a market for live killer whales, and several hundred were captured off British Columbia in 1962-73, and a further 59 off Iceland in 1979-88. The animals off Iceland were mostly caught

The name "staurkval" (pole whale) refers to the large dorsal fin of the males which stands out of the water like a pole.

with the help of a modified net, mainly during the herring fishery when the killer whales often approach the herring nets and help themselves to readily available fish.

The killer whales quickly became a popular feature in aquariums around the world. They proved intelligent, quick to learn and cooperative. This has had a great deal to say for the changed view on killer whales over the last 40 years. By degrees, it has proved possible to get them to reproduce in captivity and the catching of live animals has almost ceased. However, Russian authorities issued permits to capture ten animals as recently as 2002.

The expertise of the Icelandic hunters was exploited again in 2000 and 2001 when seven killer whales were caught to attach satellite transmitters to them as part of a Norwegian research project.

Typical for how people viewed killer whales at the turn of the century was the attempt

to return Keiko – the killer whale that starred in the film "Free Willy" – to a life as a "free" whale in the ocean. The enormous use of resources and the fact that Keiko was attributed human qualities, such as an active desire to be free, nevertheless made the project highly controversial.

Another expression of the relationship of modern human beings to these fascinating creatures is the great interest for experiencing wild killer whales in their proper element. Whale safaris have become a significant industry in many parts of the world. In Norway, the first tentative attempts at organised killer whale safaris

started in Lofoten in 1985. In 1992, trips started in Tysfjord, where they became a huge success. After more than ten seasons, this has developed into well-organised ecotourism. The number of people who want to go out to see the killer whales is still growing.

A group of killer whales and a fishing-boat in Tysfjord.

Close encounters with killer whales. Killer whale safaris have become popular in Northern Norway.

Two young individuals surfing the waves behind a Zodiac during Killer whale safari in Tysfjord in 2001.

RESEARCH ON KILLER WHALES

KILLER WHALES have a long life span and a slow reproduction rate. Research on several aspects of their life history and ecology must take place over a long period, and even though they have been studied for more than thirty years, many questions about their life still remain unanswered.

The investigations of the killer whale populations along the west coast of Canada started in 1970 and form the basis for modern killer whale research throughout the world. In 1973, Dr. Michael Bigg discovered what was to revolutionise all research into killer whales, namely that each individual whale carries characteristic marks. The shape of the dorsal fin, and nicks and notches on it, along with the shape of the grey saddle patch behind the dorsal fin and scars on it, constitute a highly individual code, just like fingerprints on human beings.

By photographing killer whales, it was possible to survey the population with a completely different degree of precision than previously. The technique proved extremely useful. Not only was it efficient for calculating the size of a population, it also provided insight into a number of aspects of killer whale biology. Photo-identification is a simple method requiring comparatively limited resources, and is today used in killer whale studies around the world.

Killer whale research continued with studies of their vocalisations, which provided an important contribution to the studies on social organisation and kinship relationships between the various groups. Dr John Ford found that the mammal- and fish-feeding killer whales had completely different sound repertoires and that each family group of the resident whales had its own dialect. Similarity in dialect has been used as a measure of the kinship existing between the groups.

Recent genetic studies have enabled a more thorough investigation of kinship between the groups. The method for retrieving DNA samples is simple. A specially constructed rifle is used to fire a hollow, cylindrical dart into the back of a whale. The dart bores into the skin and upper blubber layer and falls out again. It floats in the sea and when it is picked up it contains a tiny sample of tissue from the whale. This sample forms the basis for a DNA analysis.

When this kind of research is performed, questions will always be raised as to whether the method will harm the animal, or visibly affect its behaviour. This was thoroughly investigated during the research in Canada and Alaska, and it was concluded that it had little effect on the whales. Indeed, their reaction was approximately the same whether the dart made contact or not. Only four individuals reacted strongly. They were all more than 35 years old, and probably had memories going back to the time before 1970 when it was common for seamen and fishermen to shoot killer whales in British Columbia.

The samples collected for DNA analysis can also be used to study the content of environmental pollutants in the blubber of the killer whales. Killer whales, being long-lived mammals on top of the food chain, are extremely vulnerable to pollutants, even in the cleanest parts of the oceans.

An important aspect is the difference in the concentration of the pollutants in females and males. Whereas males accumulate higher and higher concentrations in their fatty tissue, females will rid themselves of some of the harmful substances through their milk, thus passing them on to their offspring during the first years of their life.

A number of behavioural studies have also been carried out on killer whales in various parts of the world. Most of these studies are systematic, standardised series of observations where different forms of activity (e.g. feeding, socialising, resting and travelling) are documented. A problem in studying whale behaviour is that the animals spend most of their time under water. In Norway, scientists have solved this problem by using a combination of underwater video filming and high frequency videosonar to reveal how the whales hunt herring. These methods have been extremely successful and the results have given new insight into interactions between a predator and its prey.

Another useful way of studying whale behaviour is to study their diving behaviour either with the help of satellite tags that are fastened to the dorsal fin of the whales and which collect and transmit information over long periods of time or with tags that are attached with a suction cup and which collect data for a shorter period (from a few hours to a few days) before they fall off. The tags can collect information on the depth and duration of the dives as well as the swimming speed and the time of the day when the dives are performed. Newly developed tags also contain a digital compass which records the orientation of the animal during the different phases of its dive, and its vocalisations. –

The seasonal migrations of killer whales often follow the migrations of their prey. For several populations, we have built up a great deal of knowledge about the periods when the whales are present in areas where their prey are concentrated, but we know little or nothing about what they do the rest of the time.

For many years, scientists have sought a good way of tagging killer whales to try to find out more about their movements throughout the year. Many obstacles have to be overcome. The first killer whale was tagged with a radio transmitter off the west coast of the USA as early as 1973 to try to use the radio signals to trace the movements of the whale. The instrument seemed to be working well, but the signals were interrupted after only eight hours by a radio report from a baseball match in Florida.

The first time killer whales were fitted with combined radio and satellite transmitters was in 2000 and 2001 when a total of seven animals were tagged off Norway. This introduced a new phase in killer whale research.

Next page:
Researchers on board the 40 feet
research vessel S/Y Iolaire.

THE LIFE OF KILLER WHALES

OVER 30 YEARS of using the photo-identification technique to study the behaviour and life history of killer whales along the Pacific Ocean coast in Canada and Alaska have given us unique information on their life history and social organisation. At first, the killer whale society was defined as a number of groupings arranged in a hierarchy which was looked upon as being stable and determined by genealogical relationships between individual animals. However, it has become clear that the links between some of these groupings are dynamic and brief, and not necessarily based on kinship. Hence, we are left with a simpler "family tree" when we want to describe the social structure of killer whales.

The basic social unit is the matrilineal group, or matriline, which consists of a female, the matriarch, and her offspring. A matriline consists of up to four generations of killer whales, which always stay close to one another. These matrilines have their own "dialects", composed of a unique selection of calls. Closely related matrilines have, to a large extent, common repertoires of calls.

Over time, a matrilineal group may split into smaller entities. This may happen when the old matriarch dies, or because the group contains a comparatively large number of reproductive females. A split generally takes place gradually through one of the older females spending more and more time with her offspring, separate from the rest of the relatives. Little by little, these sub-groups will also develop specific elements in their vocabulary, so that in the longer term they will establish their own dialects.

A "clan", or "acoustic clan", consists of matrilines that share one or more calls, indicating that they have a common ancestor.

A killer whale community consists of all the matrilineal groups that socialise with one another and form a breeding population. A community may consist of one or more acoustic clans.

Not all killer whale communities are alike. The ecology of the killer whales, particularly their choice of prey, is of great importance; much of the behaviour and structure of the groups are adapted to their menu. Along the west coast of North America, there are three communities of fish-feeding killer whales, which live in stable matrilineal groups with a dialect structure as described above. These have been called "residents" because they are seen year after year when the salmon occur in coastal waters. However, in the same area, there are killer whales which have specialised on hunting marine mammals, mainly seals, porpoises and dolphins.

Because the mammal-feeding killer whales hunt in groups, and each individual prey item represents a limited amount of food, these animals live in smaller groups. In other words, some of them must leave their matriline as it grows. Which individuals leave is decided by the age and gender composition of the matriline. Females never live alone, and when they are adults they always have some of their offspring with them. However, males have been observed hunting marine mammals alone. These males may have transient relationships with other groups, but no stable affiliation to any particular group.

The killer whales which eat marine mammals have been named as the "transients" since they do not occur as stably in an area as the fish-feeding killer whales. This is because they exploit several different marine mammal populations in the waters between Alaska and California.

The mammal-feeding killer whales are far less vocally active and have a more limited repertoire of calls than the fish feeders. An important reason for this is that mammals and fish react differently when they hear killer whales. Seals and whales will be alerted by communicating killer whales. Consequently, mammal feeders hunt in silence. Fish feeders, on the other hand, often communicate actively during the hunt..

In addition to these two, a third form, or ecotype, of killer whales has been discovered in this area during the last ten years; they are called the "offshores"., These whales live pelagically, far from the coast. They seem to live in large groups and consume small, shoaling fish, but little is known about their life since they seldom approach close to the coast and are difficult to monitor.

Along the west coast of North America, there are three separate communities of mammal-feeding killer whales, three of fish-feeding killer whales and one community of pelagic killer whales.

In many mammals, the combination of the danger of inbreeding and direct competition for food resources causes family groups to break up. So why do fish-feeding killer whales live in stable family groups and relatively small communities composed of related animals?

Probably one of the reasons is that learned skills are an important part of their lives. Hunting methods adapted to the choice of prey made by the population have to be learnt. The same goes for the dialects and the use of sounds, which play an important role in the social life of killer whales. These are complex learning processes, and learning in a large group is more advantageous than learning from their parent alone.

In such small communities as the killer whales live in – often only a few hundred individuals – the danger of inbreeding is always a real threat. Whales are doomed if they mate freely and fortuitously within their population. The specific dialects of the matrilines have an important function in connection with mating. The female probably chooses who she will mate with and, to avoid inbreeding, she selects a male with a dialect that differs from her own.

Genetic studies from the Pacific Ocean suggest that mainly old, experienced males have the chance to mate. This is not particularly surprising. In an animal society where experience is an important quality, the females will prefer to mate with a male who has shown that he is able to live a long time.

Competition for food is not a problem for the fish-feeding killer whales. They hunt fish which occur in large aggregations, but with seasonal and distributional variations. In such a setting, the location of, and exchange of information about, prey is important, and in that context living in stable groups is an advantage. There is no indication of competition or aggressive behaviour between family groups; it is more likely that cooperation and change of useful information takes place between the groups.

Because fish-feeding killer whales avoid inbreeding and do not compete for food, the relative profitability of dispersal is less, and quite small populations may be viable.

NORWEGIAN KILLER WHALES

— RESEARCH ON KILLER WHALES ALONG
THE COAST OF NORWAY

OUR KNOWLEDGE about marine mammals used to be based on hunting statistics and information gathered from dead animals. These data form important reference material for modern research, which is based on long-term studies on live individuals. This research has been taking place since the early 1980s, inspired by the long-term research project on killer whales in the Pacific Northwest. When the research started, little was known about the behavioural ecology of killer whales in Norway and there were many questions we wanted to find answers to. Is there a single Norwegian killer whale population, or are there more? Do Norwegian killer whales live in stable family groups? Are the calls of killer whales in Norwegian waters like those of other killer whales? Do Norwegian killer whales live solely on fish, or do they also feed on marine mammals? What is the range of the whales throughout the year?

Killer Whales have a complex social life, and a large repertoire of activities. This playful calf from the NT-group was photographed off Vesterålen, summer 1991.

Most behavioural studies of Norwegian killer whales are based on observations made when the animals come to the surface to breathe.

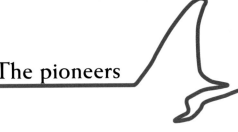

The pioneers

At the beginning of the 1980s, two Swedes, Mic Calvert and Stefan Ostrowski, went to the USA and Canada to watch whales and find out how tourism and research were combined. They had founded the Centre for Studies of Whales and Dolphins (CSVD) – a network of artists and scientists who were interested in whales. In Vancouver, they met the whale biologist John Ford. He could not understand why they had travelled all the way to Canada to see killer whales when they could find them in their own vicinity, in Lofoten in Norway.

That settled it. Mic and Stefan went to Lofoten and Vestfjord in 1982, and when the autumn and herring came, they made their first observations of Norwegian killer whales. They spent several autumn seasons in Lofoten, but their plans did not get really off the ground before Mic bought an old wooden fishing boat, "Old Bi", in Denmark and sailed it from Gothenburg to Lofoten in the late summer of 1986.

He was now accompanied by two biologists, Thomas Lyrholm and Morten Lindhardt, and they made their base in Henningsvær. Inspired by the work done in Canada, the aim was to do photo-identification and make sound recordings of killer whales, and this formed the basis for the first modern studies of killer whales in Norway. They also took paying guests onboard with them, and hence were the first to attempt killer whale safaris in this country.

One of the highlights was when they succeeded in making the first sound recordings of killer whales. In their enthusiasm, they ran to the nearest phone and rang John Ford – the man who, following his discovery of the killer whale dialects, had asked scientists working on killer whales in other parts of the world to make sound recordings.

– I suppose it raised some eyebrows when three young men squeezed into a telephone box on the market square in Henningsvær one dark November evening and held a tape recorder close to the telephone mouthpiece, and the curious sounds made by killer whales poured out into the driving snow, Mic Calvert says. – Not to mention John Ford's surprise when he was woken up at an unearthly hour in his bed in Vancouver to hear wind forming the background to sounds made by killer whales he'd never heard before.

One of the guests during that very first season of killer whale safaris in Norway was Tiu Similä. She was one of the paying guest who also assisted with the photo-identification, and she clearly remembers the time on "Old Bi" and her first meeting with the killer whales.

– We were a small but diverse group on "Old Bi". The crew was composed of artists and biologists. And we were four "tourists" – Tuukka, a geography student, and myself from Finland, and a young engineer, Federico, and a pensioned submarine captain from Italy. The submarine captain had come here to experience these creatures which he thought had many similarities with submarines – both spend most of their time under water and have good sonar! He regaled us with

countless tales of his days as a prisoner-of-war in England. The only thing he disliked was the morning porridge, because he had had his fill of that in the prison camp. Federico, Tuukka and I were "hooked" on whales. The biologists were aiming to start a long-term study, and the artists, who would subsequently build up the first whale watching tourism in Andenes, were there to experience the Lofoten Wall, the sea and the charismatic animals.

Tiu remembers her first meeting with the killer whales as a fantastic experience. – I came out of pure curiosity. As a marine biologist, I was obviously fascinated by the sea, and the idea of meeting killer whales was alluring. However, I was completely unprepared for that first meeting. We were out in rough sea in a half-sinking rubber dinghy off Henningsvær and had just been thinking of returning to the harbour when a huge dorsal fin suddenly pierced the water alongside the boat. It belonged to a big male, which was identified in the first season and given the name NB-6. It swam past us at close range, and I was speechless.

– I had seen big mammals before, but those observations had been different. I had to make myself invisible and inaudible to catch a glimpse of the animals. Here I was in close contact with an enormous killer whale and it was scarcely reacting to my presence.

– In the weeks that followed, I was out helping to photograph killer whales and in the evenings I listened to the biologists telling of the results of a long-term study of killer whales around Vancouver Island in Canada. Matriarchal societies, dialects, specialised feeding behaviour – after a few days I knew this was what I wanted to do research on, and the thought of continuing research on plankton in small Finnish lakes suddenly became very remote....

However, the whale safari operation from Henningsvær never became a great success, for either scientists or tourists, because it was difficult to get regular observations of killer whales here. So while the biologists went on to other corners of the world, it was the young biology student, Tiu, who chose to settle in North Norway and take up the work which the pioneers from the 1980s had begun. However, her research did not get seriously off the ground before a few years passed and it was discovered that, a little later in the autumn, the killer whales were concentrated in Tysfjord.

IDENTIFICATION

THE PHOTO-IDENTIFICATION and cataloguing of killer whales began around Lofoten and Vesterålen in 1983, and the work is still in progress. More than 550 individuals have been identified, most of them in the autumn in Tysfjord, Ofotfjord and Vestfjord. The long-term database on individually known whales has become a valuable aid for studying the occurrence, behaviour and social structure of Norwegian killer whales.

The identification catalogue needs to be continuously revised, new animals are born into the various groups each year, and calves grow up. Males, in particular, change in appearance as they grow and do not become fully grown until they are around 20 years old. The growth of the dorsal fin speeds up when the males are around 15 years old. Although the fin grows in height, cuts and nicks will remain visible as long as the whale lives. New marks may be added, but old ones will never disappear.

The catalogue of identified animals forms the basis for much of the research on killer whales in Norway. Each individual has a code name consisting of two letters and one digit. The family group, or matriline, is named after the individual that was described first.

The main aims of the identification work have been to obtain the best possible estimate of the population, and to study the social organisation and ecology of Norwegian killer whales.

30 different family groups were catalogued in 1986-93, and the structure in the groups was stable, as we find among the Canadian fish-feeding killer whales.

The total size of the killer whale population along the Norwegian coast is not known. However, the population that follows the herring, and is mainly observed in the wintering fjords in Nordland in the autumn and on the herring spawning grounds on the Møre coast in spring, can be estimated at around 1500. Killer whales are also regularly observed along the coast of Finnmark and sporadically as far north as Svalbard, and there are strong indications that these belong to a different population from that which follows the herring. Killer whales are observed further south, too, in the southern part of the Norwegian Sea and in the North Sea, and we know very little about the identity or ecology of these whales.

Two big males;
NN-17 (right) and NN-25
in Tysfjord on November 11th 2002.

This group was first seen in Tysfjord in 1989, and has been observed each autumn since then, except for 1997. The same whales were also seen off Vesterålen in July 1991.

NE15 is an easy group to study, since it is a small matriline. NE-17 is the matriarch. She often keeps her distance from research vessels, and seems to know the whereabouts of the rest of the group. She has not had any calves since 1992 and is assumed to be over 50 years old. NE-17 is probably the mother of NE-15 (born in 1973 or earlier), NE-18 (born about 1978), NE-24 and NE-55 (born in 1992).

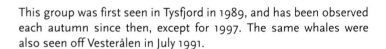

*NE-17, the matriarch
of the family group,
photographed in 2003*

*NE-15,
the matriarchs oldest living son,
photographed in 2003*

*NE-18, son of NE-17,
probably born in 1978,
photographed in 1991*

She also had a calf around 1986-87, but this had died in 1992, when she had her last calf (NE-55).

There are two adult males in the NE15 group, NE-15 (the first in the group to be identified, thus giving the group its name) and NE-18. NE-15 was fully grown in 1989, and must therefore be at least 30 years old (born in 1973 or earlier). NE-18 reached "puberty" in 1991, and was probably born in 1978.

NE-24 had a calf in 2001. She probably also had one or two calves in the 1990s, which are now dead.

NE-55 has proved to be a female. On 20 November 2003, she was observed with a calf that had just been born. "Uncle" NE-15 showed this calf a great deal of care and consideration, and always swam between it and the research vessel. It will be exciting to see whether this calf survives, because it is unfortunately often the case that the first offspring of young females dies, and NE-55, being only 11 years old, is an extremely young mother.

This small matriline is thus slowly, but steadily, growing. However, NE-15 is beginning to be an old male, and his mother, NE-17, is a "grand old lady", so it is not certain we will see them again in the coming autumns.

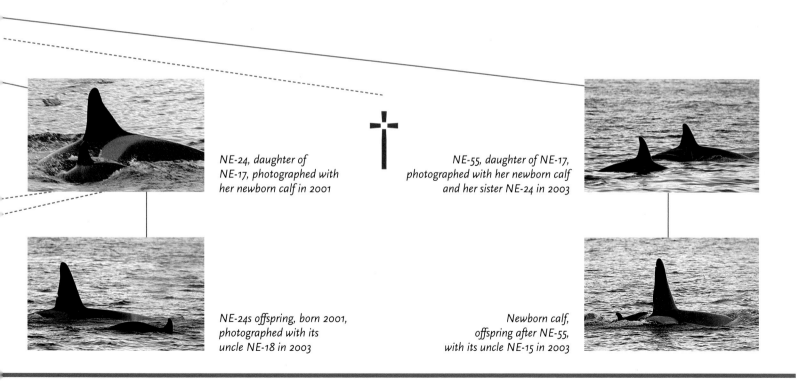

NE-24, daughter of NE-17, photographed with her newborn calf in 2001

NE-55, daughter of NE-17, photographed with her newborn calf and her sister NE-24 in 2003

NE-24s offspring, born 2001, photographed with its uncle NE-18 in 2003

Newborn calf, offspring after NE-55, with its uncle NE-15 in 2003

ACOUSTIC STUDIES

THE DISCOVERY OF group specific dialects among killer whales in Pacific Northwest inspired researchers in other parts of the world to start recording the vocal repertoire of local killer whale populations.

The first recordings in Norwegian waters were made in 1985 and showed that Norwegian killer whales produce the same types of sounds as the fish-feeding killer whales in British Columbia comprising of whistles, calls and echolocation clicks.

A study based on the first Norwegian recordings supported what was called the "Big Bang Theory". According to this theory, toothed whales are able to produce sounds which are powerful enough to stun fish. Loud bangs were recorded while Norwegian killer whales were feeding on herring, and stunned herring floating on the surface were interpreted as support for this theory.

It was not before 1991, when feeding behaviour of Norwegian killer whales was first filmed, that it was discovered that the bangs were produced by powerful slaps which the whales inflicted on the herring shoal with their tails to stun herring.

Several new sound recordings were made in Vestfjord and Tysfjord between 1986 and 1992 and, although the number of recordings per group was quite limited, the data suggested that Norwegian killer whales also have dialects. Many different calls were described, and complex series made up of several call sounds arranged in a specific system were recognised.

Comparisons were made between nine matrilines, and all of them shared at least one call signal – most of them several. The NN group stood out as the only one with just one call signal in common with the others.

The Norwegian killer whale calls were then compared with those from other areas. A few similarities were found with calls used by killer whales from Norway and Iceland, British Columbia and Alaska, but this could be pure chance. However, the most interesting feature was that the NN pod shared several calls with Icelandic killer whales. This may indicate that NN is closely related to Icelandic matrilines.

The NN group appears in North Norway later than the other groups. Whereas most groups follow the herring into the fjords in October-November, NN whales have usually appeared after Christmas. November 2001 was the first time the group came before Christmas, and that was nearly ten years after it was first observed in the Vestfjord area.

The structure of the calls made by Norwegian killer whales has been compared with those made by animals from Iceland and British Columbia. The duration and number of calls were studied and, whereas killer whales from Canada had more and shorter call signals, there was no difference between the structure in Norwegian and Icelandic killer whales. This suggests that Icelandic and Norwegian killer whales are closely related and may have made up a common population not so very long ago. Several factors explain why the study of the repertoire of sounds made by Norwegian killer whales is still in its infancy and has not yet produced any firm conclusions, even though a great deal of work has been done. First and foremost, a vast number of animals are gathered in the areas where the whales have been studied. In many contexts this is an advantage, but it causes difficulties when you want to survey the acoustic repertoire of just one group. There are often several family groups in close vicinity of each other and therefore it is not easy to obtain recordings of just one group. Another practical problem is the large number of boats (fishing boats, ferries, tourist boats) in the fjords – noise created by engines often makes it impossible to obtain good quality recordings.

Behavioural studies

THE BEHAVIOUR OF a killer whale population is closely related to their choice of prey. The killer whales that have been studied in Norway feed on Norwegian spring-spawning herring, and follow the seasonal migrations of the shoals.

Their behaviour has been studied mainly in autumn and winter, when both the herring and the whales are concentrated in a limited area in Vestfjord, Ofotfjord and Tysfjord. The days are shortening then, and the light is steadily getting poorer. The project in Norway is the only one taking place north of the Arctic Circle that is based on photo-identification in winter!

On the other hand, conditions for underwater observations are ideal. The herring do not come to these fjords to eat – there is very little plankton in the water at this time of year – they are merely there to spend the winter. Hence, there are large numbers of killer whales and herring, and no plankton or other organisms to reduce visibility in the water. The crystal clear water offers the chance to use underwater cameras to study the interactions between killer whales and herring, giving unique opportunities to study both the hunting

behaviour of the killer whales and the defence mechanisms of the herring. Naturally, much of the research has therefore been focused on the interaction between herring and killer whales.

In spring, most of the killer whales probably follow the adult herring to their spawning grounds off the coast of Møre and Trøndelag, hundreds of kilometres further south in Norway. In summer, both the herring and the killer whales are dispersed over large areas, and less is known of the behavioural pattern in that period.

Several studies of the behaviour of Norwegian killer whales have been based on observations made when the animals come to the surface to breathe. Systematic records have been made of breathing intervals, swimming speeds and directions, the behaviour of individuals and the spatial organisation of the group – whether all the animals swim in the same direction or in different directions.

These observations have enabled the general behaviour of the killer whales to be divided into four broad categories: feeding, resting, travelling and socialising. These

categories can be used to observe general patterns, but they give limited insight for a detailed understanding of their behaviour.

As with other long-living, social mammals, it is impossible to ignore the fact that killer whales are first and foremost individuals. We can generalise their behaviour to a certain extent, but the more we go into detail, the more it is a matter of individual behaviour.

Killer whales are extremely social animals. Much of the social activity is based on vocal communication. The killer whales also have very sensitive skin, and physical contact is an important part of their social interaction. After they have eaten, they often spend time relaxing, playing and socialising. On underwater films, we have often seen how they touch one another with their flippers and dorsal fin, and how one animal strokes its stomach against the side of another. In particular, we see that calves from one

A curious killer whale watching the research vessel S/Y Iolaire.

Sometimes big males act as "assistants" for small calves. This is NA-25 assisting the offspring of one of the females in the family group.

or more family groups enjoy each other's company and play together.

At such times, we often see killer whales surface to have a look at us – do a "spyhop". Several individuals may surface at the same place, often synchronised so that they "pop up" simultaneously. Such behaviour is often observed when the whales are hunting and one or more boats approach close to their quarry. However, it usually seems as though they simply think it entertaining to take a look above the water. On underwater recordings, we have seen how spy hopping is combined with somersaulting and other forms of play beneath the surface.

Some family groups, and young whales in general, are very curious about boats. They can react to whistling and other sounds made by whale-watchers. Killer whales also enjoy the current made by propellers, and it is common to see them following in the stream of bubbles made by the propellers behind boats. It is a fantastic experience for whale-watchers to see how they react to the proximity of people, follow the boat and really show off. However, it is important to consider whether whales should be encouraged to follow boats, since they cannot distinguish a whale-watching vessel that is careful of how it navigates near them from another boat that may unintentionally injure a whale that comes too close to its propeller.

A small group consisting of very young animals often separates from a family group that is feeding on herring. The young ones are there to learn, do not eat much and cannot be bothered to stay long. Instead, they form small "playgroups" some distance from the feeding adults. The adults, especially females, keep a watchful eye on such situations. If any of the juveniles wander too far away, or visit boats, they are often fetched back.

Young, playful killer whales may also tease adults by swimming above them, pushing and cavorting. The adults may then put them in place by striking their tail fin powerfully on the surface. Such a signal may also be directed at a boat which comes too close, and is an obvious expression of irritation. Blows with the tail may also form part of play, and it requires long experience with killer whales to distinguish between "irritated" and "playful" strikes with the tail.

In addition to the "playgroups", we quite often see two or three males swimming together on their own, behaving playfully. They touch each other, and under water we see that they are swimming in a spiralling motion. During such behaviour, it is not unusual to see that one or more of them has an erected penis. We do not know the function of this behaviour; perhaps it is a way of strengthening the bonds between males in a family group, but it may also be a form of competition. We know little about the possible existence of hierarchy in a killer whale family. We know that an older female, the matriarch, leads the group, but we do not whether any other ranking exists in the rest of the group.

Killer whales spend most of their time moving around, seeking food or just travelling. This activity constitutes a significant part of the everyday life of the killer whale, especially in summer, probably because the herring are much more widely dispersed then. Nevertheless, even when food is available in large quantities, the whales spend a great deal of time moving around.

Occasionally, adult males are seen acting as "assistants" for small calves, particularly when the group is travelling. The males, uncles or older brothers, have the very youngest calves with them. The calves swim close to the sides of the males, thus gaining a hydrodynamic advantage.

The Norwegian research has mostly concentrated on the hunting techniques of killer

*Killer whales showing different social activities
– probably behaviour of both
playful and sexual character.*

A young male killer whale breaching and showing his erected penis.

"Stumpy"

The story of "Stumpy" is an example of the insight we can gain into the life of killer whales through long-term observations of known individuals.

"Stumpy" is a young killer whale who was born in 1995. He was first observed in Tysfjord in 1996, and he then had serious injuries to his spine and dorsal fin. He was in the company of his mother, and they were swimming close to the NE15 group, but the mother is not a member of that group.

We did not see "Stumpy" again for several years and assumed he had not survived his extensive injuries. Then, in 2002, he was suddenly back in Tysfjord. We now got more and better pictures of him and were able to see that his left side was badly damaged. He appeared to have been hit by a boat when he was a small calf.

We have several observations of "Stumpy" when he was 7-8 years old, and his behaviour tells us that he is not like other killer whales. A killer whale of that age is normally attached to its mother and its family group, but instead of swimming with his family, "Stumpy" swims with

a variety of groups. We have identified at least five different groups which have been looking after him. Both in 2002 and 2003, he was seen several times with the NE15 group, and it was particularly interesting that on those occasions he was accompanied by an adult male who did not belong to the group. It seems as though "Stumpy" feels a strong bond to the NE15 group, perhaps his own family group broke away from it. But why this adult male is with "Stumpy" when he is with the NE15 group is a mystery.

When the killer whales are feeding, "Stumpy" generally remains on the edge of the group. His deformed spine probably prevents him diving properly, but we have still not succeeded in obtaining observations and film of his movements under water. Even though he is unable to take part in pursuing herring, he obviously gets enough food. He probably eats some of the herring that have been stunned by the other animals in the group he is accompanying. There are also two observations of adults taking a herring to "Stumpy".

In addition to ensuring that "Stumpy" gets food, it is very obvious that the adults he is with protect him. It is not easy to get near him with a boat. One or two adult whales are generally between "Stumpy" and the boat, and on several occasions we have seen them push him away from boats, or swim up beside him and guide him away from them.

Since killer whales live in family groups with strong bonds between individuals, it is perhaps not so strange that "Stumpy" is looked after. Nevertheless, it is surprising that a disabled individual is being taken care of by several groups. Even though he was seen with his mother the first year, we do not know her identity, and consequently nor do we know which family group "Stumpy" originally belongs to.

It will be exciting to see what happens to him when he becomes sexually mature and an adult – whether he will still be looked after by others.

The first photo of "Stumpy", from 1996.

"Stumpy" with the NR group, resting while the other animals are hunting.

"Stumpy" being led away by members of the NR group.

whales. Several million tonnes of herring congregate in the over-wintering area – the killer whales are literally swimming in food – and it might be thought that it would be easy for the whales to get their fill of herring. But this is not the case.

It has been known for a long time that killer whales hunt herring by pressing them together in compact 'balls'. One would think that faced with a densely aggregated herring shoal, all the whales would have to do was open their jaws and help themselves to a mouthful at a time. Baleen whales, such as fin and humpback whales, have evolved such a technique. They trap fish schools in their mouth and filter the water out through their baleens. Killer whales, however, are unable to capture herring in schools in this manner. They have to gain control over smaller schools and then stun herring so that they can eat individual fish.

The killer whales have several ways of herding herring into small, compact schools. They can begin by chasing a large shoal into shallow water near land, or up against an underwater ridge that acts as a barrier. Places with such underwater ridges are common feeding sites for killer whales.

Early in the day, after the herring have begun their diurnal migration downwards, a few shoals often remain closer to the surface. When the killer whales find such shoals, they split them into smaller ones and force them up towards the surface where they are easier to control. The use of sound is important when herring are herded, and the whales also keep the herring together by exposing the white patches on their bellies and blowing bubbles while encircling the school.

What happens when the whales have succeeded in gathering the herring close to the surface is a spectacular sight. The herring school is so close to the surface that the sea seems to be "boiling" with fish, at times some of the fish jumps out of the sea to try to escape the encircling whales. During such "carousel feeding", the whales strike the tightly packed ball of herring with their tails to stun the fish, which they then eat one by one.

The first time we saw how the whales behave during carousel feeding was in 1991 when a British film photographer, Peter Scoones, using a specially constructed underwater camera mounted on a rubber dinghy, managed to film feeding behaviour of the killer whales for the first time.

In 1992, the research team used a similar underwater camera equipped with hydrophones. New, fantastic footage was

Sometimes the killer whales chase herring out of the water.

produced. It was possible to see how the whales surrounded the herring shoal and gathered it into a dense ball which they forced up towards the surface by displaying their white bellies and expelling air bubbles. Then they struck the school with their tails, stunning several fish. The whales then swam gracefully among the stunned fish and picked out herring one by one. The footage also revealed that the loud bangs heard while the whales are carousel feeding are produced by the tailslaps.

Until recently, we knew little about the diving capability of Norwegian killer whales. In 1993, their feeding behaviour was studied with the help of a high-frequency video-sonar system that could follow them into the depths. This equipment enabled us to study the interaction between herring and whales at greater depths than previously. Nevertheless, it only gave us a glimpse of the behaviour because it was impossible to follow the whales for long periods. It was the tagging of killer whales in 2000 and 2001 that first gave us more insight, because most of the tags also held an instrument that recorded diving behaviour.

One theory had been that an important role for the males in the group was to perform the deepest and longest dives, since they are bigger and have capacity to dive longer and deeper than the females. However, here, too, we were to get a surprise; the young females undertook the longest and deepest dives. The very deepest went down to 312 metres and lasted between seven and eight minutes.

The instruments told us that the deepest dives were undertaken in daytime when the herring are deep in the water, and we believe that the purpose of the dives is to bring herring closer to surface. To do this, the whales need to expend much more energy than when they feed on herring found closer to the surface. Consequently, it is not surprising that the whales mainly hunt herring that are more readily available. More than half of the recorded dives do not exceed 12 metres and only about a tenth go beyond 20 metres.

In recent years, it has also been shown how the killer whales have learnt new techniques in their pursuit of the herring. The herring fishery has expanded greatly since the early 1990s, and the killer whales have had to share their fishing grounds with an ever-expanding herring fleet. When a purse seiner hauls in a net full of herring, it uses a large pump to get the fish onboard. The sound of the pump seems to act like a food bell for killer whales; they can hear it at least as far as 12 kilometres away! While

The rubber dinghy with the specially constructed underwater video-camera in 1992.

Sequences from the video-recordings showing killer whales carousel feeding.

the pumping is taking place, some fish slip out of the net. They are worn out and are easy prey for the killer whales, which can get a free meal without elaborate herding of herring. Herring fishing mostly takes place in twilight and darkness, and it was not before some killer whales could be followed by satellites and radio transmitters that this behaviour was documented. This is also a reminder of the limitations of studies based on visual observations in the Arctic winter.

Occasionally, killer whales also get into the net itself, when it is set in an area where killer whales are feeding on a herring shoal. The whales can get in and out of herring nets with surprising ease, but often with a damaged net as a result.

Killer whales that hunt marine mammals in Norwegian waters are mostly known to us from reports by fishermen and whalers. Several of these are detailed and highly trustworthy eye-witness accounts.

Killer whales were twice observed attacking bottlenose whales in northern waters in the 1960s. In one instance, north-west of Spitsbergen, whalers who had just shot a bottlenose whale saw killer whales in the vicinity eating another one that had recently died. Two of the killer whales, one on each side, held the bottlenose whale afloat while the others ate. When the whalers tried to approach to see whether it was possible to obtain some of the meat and blubber from the dead animal, the killer whales disappeared and the bottlenose whale sank. However, as soon as they withdrew, the killer whales retrieved the carcass and continued to feed on the surface.

On another occasion, at the ice edge close to Jan Mayen, a whaler had harpooned two bottlenose whales, both of which were still alive when killer whales appeared and attacked them close to the vessel. Some of the killer whales took a firm hold with their teeth on the fins and tails of the bottlenose whales, while others attacked the helpless creatures. However, the attack was disrupted when the whalers shortened the lines so that the dying bottlenose whales could be killed at the side of the vessel.

In summer 2004, there was a report of killer whales attacking a harpooned minke whale at the ice edge close to Svalbard. Two large males were observed a fair distance from the whaler. The whaler pursued and shot a minke whale. It made a quick turn and then accelerated enormously in a final dive. As it surfaced, the two killer whales were ready and waiting, and placed themselves on top of it, and shortly afterwards the minke was dead. The killer whales then followed for a while whilst the minke was winched in, but they gave up when it came close to the side of the vessel.

These cases provide support for a number of accounts from Norwegian whalers of bottlenose and minke whales that lack some or all of their flippers. Even when the wounds have completely healed, the marks of killer whale teeth have still been clearly visible. Such marks are also known from the tail fins of sperm whales and humpback whales, and can be seen on photographs of the tails. These accounts seem to indicate that even when killer whales attack other whales, it is by no means certain that they will succeed in killing them.

Attacks on seals are also known from Norwegian waters. During photo-identification work on killer whales off the Møre coast, killer whales which were pursuing or feeding on seals were observed on three occasions. In July 1987, five were observed for more than ten minutes hunting common seals close to a colony, without it being possible to ascertain whether the hunt was successful. In October 1990, four killer whales were seen eating fresh blubber close to a grey seal colony. Moreover, in March 1991, five were seen swimming close to land, and one of them surfaced with a harbour seal in its mouth, although it was impossible to prove that the seal was devoured.

Interestingly, these whales were identified and all of them belonged to the KI matriline. It seemed likely that they were members of a different, mammal-feeding population, but animals from the KI group were also observed on two occasions in 1991 while pursuing herring along with other killer whales. Hence, the KI matriline proved to be a group that alternates between eating fish and marine mammals. We do not yet know whether this is common among Norwegian killer whales, or whether KI has developed a unique habit.

Another observation suggesting that Norwegian fish-feeding killer whales also may hunt marine mammals is from June 1993, from the island of Røst in Lofoten. A group of killer whales was observed circling a rock on which a lone harbour seal was resting while the tide was rising. The seal survived because the tide did not completely cover the rock and the whales gave up after an hour and a half. The group was identified using photographs and proved to be the NØ matriline, which has been encountered on several occasions in the Tysfjord area where it was hunting herring in the autumn.

Too much significance must not be placed on just one observation from northern Norway. Nevertheless, there are several detailed eye-witness accounts from Røst of killer whales attacking and killing seals. This may indicate that the observations of the KI group on the Møre coast are not isolated cases and that more Norwegian killer whales may alternate between feeding on herring and marine mammals.

It might be thought that the killer whale, being the only whale that eats other marine mammals and which, in other parts of the world, takes whales much larger than itself, would have no fear whatsoever of other animals in the sea. However, there is one exception; killer whales avoid long-finned pilot whales!

The long-finned pilot whale is smaller than the killer whale. It lives in large schools, often numbering several hundred individuals, and dives and hunts at great depths. There is no evidence to suggest that pilot whales eat marine mammals, although they have been observed off Andøya in Northern Norway in summer attacking both humpback and sperm whales, species that are far larger than the pilot whale. None of the large whales were killed, and the reason for the attacks is unclear.

Pilot whales regularly appear in the Vestfjord area in autumn and the killer whales then avoid that area. From 1991 to 2002, as many as 36 observations were made of killer whales at high speed – in excess of 10 knots – fleeing areas where pilot whales were present. Reports of killer whales avoiding pilot whales are also known from Gibraltar.

Why does the apparently supreme killer whale avoid the far smaller pilot whale?

Maybe pilot whales are "the bullies of the seas". They arrive in large schools and display aggressive behaviour towards other whales. Perhaps the motivation is competition for the same food resources, but that scarcely explains the relationship to the killer whales since pilot whales feed mainly on squid and deep-water fish. However, pilot whales are tremendously vocal, and it may be that a large number of them make so much noise that the killer whales flee to quieter areas.

Whatever the explanation, the behaviour observed when these two species of whales meet one another is extremely interesting, and perhaps observations of direct confrontations between killer whales and pilot whales will eventually throw more light on the relationship between them.

Pilot whales in the Vestfjord in October 1999. For three days some 300 animals were seen around the island of Skrova. Despite energetic search, no killer whales were seen in the area as long as the pilot whales were around.

THE MIGRATIONS OF HERRING AND KILLER WHALES

THE NORWEGIAN SPRING-SPAWNING herring is a fatty, nutritious fish, with a present biomass of about 6 million tonnes. It is therefore a key prey species for several predators in the Norwegian Sea, including killer whales.

Nevertheless, herring do not constitute such a stable and predictable food resource as their large numbers might lead us to believe. The herring stock can go through substantial changes in size and spatial distribution over time, as fishermen have experienced over the years.

The Norwegian spring-spawning herring has an annual cycle composed of spawning, feeding and over-wintering. After spawning along the Norwegian coast in spring, the herring migrate far out into the Norwegian Sea where they feed all summer. The herring feeds in areas with high primary production and their main prey is a copepod (Calanus finmarchicus). When this plankton production declines towards the autumn, the herring move to areas where they enter their over-wintering phase. By that time, they have built up fat reserves and developed roe and milt.

The most dramatic shift in the migration pattern of the herring in modern times took place during the 1960s. Prior to that, the herring spent the winter in the open sea east of Iceland and near Bear Island, and spawned on the coast of western Norway. However, in 1963 the younger year-classes of herring changed their migration pattern and started to spend the winter in the waters off the county of Troms before spawning on the Røst fishing bank and in Vestfjord, and migrating out to feed in the Norwegian Sea. This division of the population, however, lasted only three years. In 1967, the "new" population migrated from its northern feeding areas to the waters east of Iceland, and joined the rest of the Norwegian herring stock.

All this took place at a time when vast quantities of herring were being fished, and in a matter of a few years the entire stock collapsed. Following that, the Norwegian herring fishery ceased, and the herring stock slowly recovered. During the 1970s herring started to winter in the coastal waters of Norway. After a slow period of growth, a great change took place in 1983, when there was the first really good year-class of herring for more than twenty years.

This year-class migrated from the feeding areas in the Barents Sea into Vestfjord in the winter of 1986-87. The following year, it migrated further up Vestfjord and spent the winter as far in as Tysfjord and Ofotfjord. In the succeeding years, several strong year-classes followed its lead and these fjords have remained the most important wintering area for the herring ever since.
The herring were followed by the killer whales, and an increasingly expanding fleet of fishing boats.

It has been claimed that the human-induced collapse of the stock forced a change in the migration pattern of the herring; that it had one over-wintering area previously and a completely different one today. However, this is an over-simplification. History tells us that the herring have shifted their over-wintering area many times over the ages. It has been thought that large herring with roe and milt have periodically approached the coast in autumn at intervals of around a century. This "big herring" was viewed as a separate strain, distinct from the "spring herring" which came to western Norway to spawn in spring. Little documentation exists from old times, but between 1860 and 1875 the big herring came to the coast of northern Norway in September, forming the basis for a substantial fishery. However, this pattern was broken in 1875, and at that time it was impossible to find out where the fish had gone. Even though herring were still fished locally in northern Norway, the huge herring fishery was an event of the past and 110 years were to pass before the fjords of Nordland were once more to become the most important fishing ground for the Norwegian herring fleet.

The Norwegian spring-spawning herring have now had their over-wintering area in the fjords for sixteen years, but there are signs indicating that parts of the population have been spending the winter in offshore waters west and north of the wintering fjords the last two years. We can only guess at what is happening. Maybe the herring have again split into two groups with separate over-wintering areas and will join up again after a few years. Or perhaps this

is a forewarning that they are in process of shifting their over-wintering area, and will in the course of a few years once more be spending their winters in the open sea.

This last possibility will fit well with the old view that the herring migrate in to spend some winters in coastal waters at intervals of about 100 years. But why is this so?

One possibility is that it is part of the long-term survival strategy of the herring, scarcely discernible in the short perspective of modern-day science. Viewed from the perspective of the herring, it may be vital that it does not spend the winter in the same area too many years in succession. During this phase, it is vulnerable to predation from a number of fish and other predators, and it may be a good tactic for the herring to periodically change their wintering areas to prevent predators learning where they may be habitually found.

In that case, perhaps the killer whales will shortly be seeking herring in entirely different areas in autumn than they do today. Such a change in the choice of the over-wintering areas of herring and killer whales is also known from Icelandic waters.

Killer whales and a fishing vessel at sunrise in Tysfjord.

A killer whale in the Vestfjord, with Mount Vågakallen in the background.

Tagging killer whales

Most of our knowledge of killer whales derives from long-term studies based on observations of individually known whales, and a common aspect of all these studies is that almost all the data have been collected in periods of the year when the killer whales are pursuing prey in coastal waters; for example in Canada and Alaska in connection with the migration of the salmon towards the coast and when seals are having their pups, and in Norway in the period when the herring are gathered in the fjords. In practice, this means that the habitat and behaviour of the killer whales in the greater part of the year has been completely unknown.

Satellite tagging of killer whales enables us to follow the animals irrespective of where they are. The tags transmit signals to satellites when the animals surface to breathe. If two or more satellites have intercepted the signal, the position of the whale can be calculated. Most tags also carry an instrument that records the number of dives undertaken, their depth and duration. This provides valuable information about the behaviour of the animals.

It has taken several years to develop tags that stand up to the strains of the marine environment and the pressure during deep dives. It has proved particularly difficult to get the antenna to function properly and to find batteries that are small and at the same time have adequate capacity. Tags that can be shot into the blubber layer can be used for large whales like blue whales, fin whales and sperm whales, but this is not possible for smaller species because their blubber layer is comparatively thin. Consequently, a method has been developed whereby the tag can be fixed into the dorsal fin. Usually, 3 or 4 holes are made in the dorsal fin, rather like we people have holes in our ears, and the tag is fastened there using plastic or metal pins. Because such tags cannot be attached from a distance, it is necessary to capture the animals for tagging. The technique has been employed mainly for animals that have stranded or been trapped in fishing gear. White whales have been captured with the aid of large nets placed close to shallow shores. However, the killer whales have represented a major challenge because they do not become trapped in fishing gear, seldom strand, and driving them towards land would expose them to great risks.

Norway was the first country to undertake satellite tagging of killer whales. A 150-foot purse seiner was used, and Icelandic experts were employed who knew how to capture killer whales alive. Their technique was evolved in the 1970s and 1980s, when many Icelandic killer whales – including Keiko – were captured to be sold to aquariums and entertainment parks.

The method exploits the fact that killer whales follow purse seiners and often feed in their vicinity, and for the most part the procedure is similar to herring fishing; a modified herring net is drawn around the whales, trapping them. The easiest way to proceed is to cooperate with another purse seiner which releases a small number of fish into the sea as it finishes pumping its catch onto the boat. While the killer whales are feeding on these fish, they can be surrounded by a net.

The net used for such a task has a larger mesh than a normal herring seine net, to let the fish out and retain the whales. When one or more whales are in the net, work has to proceed rapidly, since it often takes a killer whale only a few minutes to find a way out of the net. The killer whales usually reacted calmly to being trapped in the net, probably because this is not an unusual situation for them.

To secure the whale that was in the net, two men paddled a rubber dinghy close up to it and fastened a soft rope round the root of its tail. It was then guided into a sling made of sail canvas, after which it could be hauled on to the fishing boat to have the tag fixed in place.

The capture and tagging is stressful for a killer whale, irrespective of how small the tag is and how well it is fastened. Consequently, the value of the tagging results must be carefully assessed for each project, and the best available techniques must be used. Developments in tagging techniques are steadily advancing and the tags used in the Norwegian project in 2000-2001 are already considered out of date.

We anxiously looked forward to the results of the tagging, and once more the killer whales were to surprise us!

We had assumed that killer whales which followed the herring into the Nordland fjords remained there as long as the herring did. However, to our great surprise, several of the tagged whales travelled far beyond their assumed over-wintering area and

Killer whales are trapped in a purse seine to be tagged with satellite transmitters.

The female "Linn" – NY-23 – is hauled up in the purse seiner "Inger Hildur".

The male "Eytor" – Nw-6 – with his satellite tag.

made a number of trips beyond Vestfjord that lasted several weeks!

The tagging of the killer whales also showed that great differences exist between both individuals and groups. Whereas most groups or individuals periodically left the herring wintering area, one group remained there throughout the winter and its range within the area was also much smaller than that of the other groups. When the group followed the herring to the Møre coast in the late winter, it chose the shortest route and once again, on the spawning grounds, it moved very little.

Since the tags only supply information from one season, we cannot know whether the behaviour is specific for each group, or whether they alternate between different strategies from season to season.

Another surprise was that we were successful in tagging a whale from the Nz group. This group had been considered to only occur sporadically in the area where the herring spend the winter, since it was only encountered three times from 1987 to 2000. The satellite tag, however, showed that this whale was present the whole time, but was extremely shy when small boats were around. Consequently, it has been almost impossible to get into contact with members of the group, and they have scarcely been recorded in the identification programme.

We do not know why some groups react like this to boats, but it may well be that memories of previous bad experiences with boats have been handed down through older members of the group.

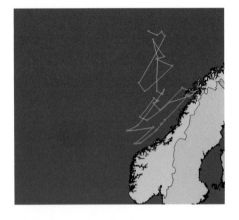

Maps showing movements of the satellite-tracked killer whales:

Upper: Daily positions of the Nz group in the herrings wintering grounds from late November till mid January. The map shows the daily movements; the distances vary between 2 and 85 kilometres.

Middle: Positions of the NW group from late November till mid June. The movements fit well with the herring migrations.

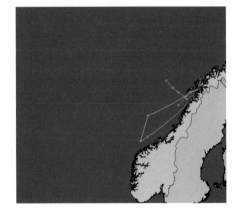

Lower: Examples of the "scouting trips" of the killer whales out of the herrings wintering grounds in December 2000. The NC group travelled Southwest to the sea off Ålesund, while the NY14 group went Northwest.

SAMPLES FOR DNA ANALYSIS

A CONSIDERABLE AMOUNT of DNA material has been collected from Norwegian killer whales in the last few years, partly in cooperation with Canadian scientists. The aims are to study the genetic structure in matrilines and the population and compare the DNA of Norwegian killer whales with that of other populations. In this respect, Icelandic killer whales are of special interest since it is not unlikely that there has been or still is contact between these populations.

In 2002, a scientist from the Norwegian Polar Institute collected samples from juvenile and adult killer whales to measure the levels of various environmental pollutants. The sampling method is the same as is employed when collecting samples for DNA analysis. A rifle is used to shoot a hollow dart into the whale. A tiny sample of blubber lodges in the hollow, and the dart falls out and floats in the water. As the pollutants are soluble in fat, they can generally be found in the blubber of marine mammals. Consequently, small blubber samples are adequate to investigate the presence of the various environmental pollutants.

The analysis of the samples from 2002 has not been completed. However, based on what we have learnt of environmental pollutants in other marine mammals, there is every reason to fear that killer whales also have high values of various pollutants.

Researchers collecting samples to measure levels of environmental pollutants in killer whales.

LIFELONG LEARNING

— THE LIFE IN STABLE FAMILY GROUPS

When we observe the highly developed hunting techniques of killer whales, adapted to different prey species, and at the same time their ability to rapidly adjust to changes in the environment, we realise that learning and experience are vital elements in their life.

The stable family group which killer whales are born into and in which they will remain throughout their life is an ideal setting for learning. A young animal will be an onlooker when the group is hunting, will imitate the adults, and will gradually take part in the actual hunt. The techniques are handed down from generation to generation. The calls, which are unique for each group and form its dialect, are passed on in the same way.

The carousel hunting technique of Norwegian killer whales is a complex behaviour which requires learning and practice. We always observe young animals in the vicinity when such hunting is taking place, and they are allowed to eat when the group has been successful. Gradually they begin to imitate the adults. They practice striking the herring with their tail, at first often missing by several metres. The technique is perfected gradually and as time goes by they can take an active part in the hunt.

The learning process is clearer still in other killer whale populations. The killer whales off the Crozet Islands have evolved a technique where they throw themselves onto the shore to catch elephant seal pups. This is not only difficult, but also dangerous, and a young killer whale would have no chance of learning such a technique by itself. The killer whales often hunt in groups, several adults together or one adult and a juvenile. Several adults hunting together generally have greater success than one hunting alone, and an adult accompanied by a juvenile has less success than an adult hunting alone. Consequently, the point of having a juvenile with them is not to enhance the success of the hunt, but rather to teach it an advanced hunting technique. On the Crozet Islands, stranding also regularly takes place when no seal pups are present, probably solely as a training exercise in the stranding technique. When such training is taking place, adult killer whales have been observed to push a juvenile onto the shore before dragging it out into the water again. In one case, a juvenile was more frequently observed with another female than its own mother. This female proved to be a great deal more successful in hunting than the mother. Is it the juvenile who chooses a better teacher, or the mother who wishes to give her offspring the best possible education? In all events, there is no doubt that the purpose of such behaviour is to teach the young killer whale.

In Australia, an entire population of dolphins has been observed to divide into two, one group continuing to live as it had for many years, while the other in the course of a few generations has learnt to live on by-catches from prawn trawlers. Today, these two populations seem to be living completely isolated from each other without any social contact or genetic exchange.

That killer whales also can be extremely adaptable – almost opportunistic – has been observed on a number of occasions when they encounter fishing activities. Groups which learnt to steal meat from whalers are well known from the industrial whaling that took place in the Antarctic in the early 1900s, and also from other waters.

Groups of killer whales which learn to steal fish from various kinds of fishing gear are also known. In Alaska, sable fish, which normally live at depths beyond the

The family group is the learning arena for young killer whales. The NB group – the matriarch NB-8 to the right.

Killer whales are often seen around fishing boats during the herring season.

The tuna-fishing fleet is the centre of attraction for the killer whales in the Straits of Gibraltar. Several groups of killer whales are known for helping themselves to large pieces of tuna before the fishermen succeed in hauling the fish aboard.

In northern Norwegian fjords where the herring overwinter, we often see killer whales spending a great deal of time around the fishing boats feeding on herring that fall out of the nets when the catch is being pumped onboard, or that slip through the nets. The herring quotas have been slowly increasing throughout the 1990s as the stock of Norwegian spring-spawning herring has grown, and the intensive fishery we see today has existed less than a decade. The Norwegian killer whales have therefore learnt in a short time that herring can be obtained in this way and adults, too, display an opportunistic ability for 'retraining'.

Similar behaviour is known among killer whales off Iceland. The whales seem to be attracted by certain sounds from the herring seiners, particularly the noise made by the large pumps when the herring are being pumped into the boat from the nets.

Not only the mother, but the whole family group becomes teachers for young individuals.

diving range of killer whales, are fished with long lines. Then, in 1985, a school of killer whales began to steal the fish when the lines were being brought up from the depths. The whales learnt to recognise the sound of the lines being hauled in and immediately swam towards them. Many means were tried to prevent this fish stealing, such as hauling in empty lines from a boat some distance from the fishing ground, but the killer whales quickly changed their tactics by dividing into several small groups, and soon the whole school knew where the fish were. After

one school had become specialised in this behaviour, other long-line fishermen in the area began to experience problems with killer whales stealing their catch, and the only solution was to carry on this fishery at a time of year when there were plenty of salmon along the coast so that the killer whales were busy hunting elsewhere.

Killer whales have also been observed stealing fish from lines off the coast of New Zealand. There it was adults who did the work, while the young animals watched and later received some of the prey.

It is not known whether it is certain family groups which have become specialised in such behaviour and created a new trend, or whether the behaviour is common to all the groups.

The fish-feeding killer whales off British Columbia hunt salmon stocks which have permanent migration routes from the open Pacific Ocean to the coast. As the whales have followed these same routes for generations, the learning partly entails locating geographical features. They have fixed 'traditions' attached to particular localities.

The Norwegian killer whales also display geographical attachment in that family groups use the same fishing spots in Tysfjord and Vestfjord year after year. However, since the herring is a species that can shift its migration pattern quite suddenly, it is not a very predictable food resource. Hence, Norwegian killer whales cannot become attached to permanent localities to the same degree as their Canadian relatives. We know the killer whales adapt to changes in the herring migration pattern, but the question is how? If they have to search at random, they may experience great problems in finding food. The tagging of killer whales with satellite transmitters in the 2000 and 2001 seasons has probably given us an answer to this question. It had been assumed that the family groups that were continually seen in the fjords from October to February were stationary in the area as long as the herring remained there. However, data from this project revealed that in the middle of the season some whales periodically leave the herring and set off on short or long trips.

Two of the tagged whales made two short trips each, both of which coincided approximately with the limit of the over-wintering area for the herring in outer Vestfjord. A more surprising observation was that four whales took much longer journeys. The minimum distance of the longest journey was as much as 1600 km. These journeys cannot be explained by changes in the availability of herring, or a switch to another type of prey, so they must have had some other purpose than foraging.

A plausible explanation is that the killer whales periodically undertake scouting trips to areas where the herring are to be found at other times of the year. The route they follow may be based on knowledge about where there is the best chance of finding the herring, which they have learnt over generations. This enables them to become aware of changes in the herring migration at such an early stage that they are quickly able to adapt to them.

Two of the four whales belonged to closely related matrilines which began their scouting trips 10 days apart. The fascinating observation was that both groups followed the same route out to the open sea. These trips were therefore not undertaken aimlessly, but the route, at least in this instance, was decided in advance. How the killer whales managed to navigate so precisely and how the route was communicated and decided between the groups is a mystery. Nor do we know why these two groups, which had remained together and hunted for most of the autumn, separated just before these scouting trips.

The scouting trips undertaken by members of different groups covered different parts of the Norwegian Sea. It is not inconceivable that killer whales can exchange information about fish occurrences, particularly between closely related groups.

The satellite tag that remained operational longest transmitted signals from November 2001 to July 2002. The positions showed how the killer whale followed the migration of the herring right up to 72 degrees North in the Norwegian Sea.

Killer whales seem to follow learned routes when they are searching the herring shoals. This is the Nc group, with Nc-1 in front, with Mount Vågakallen in the background.

Keiko

Keiko is undoubtedly the most famous whale in the world, and was the first killer whale people have tried to return to a life in the wild.

He was caught in 1979, about two years old. At that time, there was a substantial demand for live killer whales for aquariums around the world. Young ones were considered especially attractive because they were easy to train. Keiko was therefore a valuable catch, and after a while he was sold to Marineland in Ontario, Canada.

However, Keiko's career was slow taking off. As the youngest of five killer whales in Marineland, he is said to have been mobbed by other killer whales, and being a slow learner lacking self-confidence he lost his market value.

Interested purchasers first appeared five years later, and Keiko was sold to the Reino Aventura Park in Mexico City for 350,000 dollars. There, he shared the pool with two dolphins and was very soon the park's principal attraction. This small pool midway between the Atlantic and Pacific Oceans was his home for the next 15 years.

Then, at the beginning of the 1990s, a manuscript turned up at Warner Brothers, about a killer whale living under poor conditions in an entertainment park and which, through friendship with a young boy, finds its way back to freedom. The company needed a lone killer whale living in rather simple surroundings in a pool that could be hired for the film shots. Keiko was the only candidate that fitted the film company's plans, and that was to radically change his life.

The film, "Free Willy", became an enormous box office hit, along with two follow-ups, and Keiko had become a film star. Hence, it was unavoidable that focus was directed at his real living conditions. They were far from good – he lived in a small pool with warm, chlorinated, artificial seawater – and there was very soon a demand for something to be done about his situation.

Many suggestions were put forward, not all equally good. Even Michael Jackson, who wrote the theme song for "Free Willy", is said to have tried to buy Keiko at one time to have him on his ranch in California.

However, in view of the content of the "Free Willy" films, it was no surprise that a widespread demand quickly arose to return Keiko to a life as a free whale. A year after the film's successful round of American cinemas, the "Free Willy – Keiko Foundation" (FWKF) was set up, with large financial contributions from, among others, Warner Brothers and a billionaire, Craig MacCaw.

Reino Aventura, which had long since realised that Keiko had no future in Mexico City, donated him to the FWKF which, on its part, was attempting to find a suitable place to begin his rehabilitation. The choice fell on the Oregon Coast Aquarium. The construction of a new pool for Keiko began there, and was ready a year later. Keiko undoubtedly benefited from the change in his environment. His health improved rapidly in the cold, fresh seawater, and with more space to move about in he quickly became fitter. Moreover, while a large team was training Keiko in the activities it was thought were important steps on the road to freedom, work was going on behind the scenes to obtain approval to move him to a fjord in Iceland.

After two years in Oregon, the approval was forthcoming and a pen for Keiko was constructed in a fjord at Vestmannaeyer in Iceland. On 9 September 1998, Keiko was once more loaded on a plane, and was flown to Iceland. The plane had its landing gear damaged while landing on Iceland, due to the enormous weight of Keiko and his tank!

After a year in the pen, it was decided that Keiko should have the use of the entire fjord by closing it off with a strong, well-anchored net. A satellite transmitter was fitted to him and he began to be taken out for trips in the open sea accompanied by a boat. The intention was that he should meet groups of wild killer whales, which frequent these waters.

In the latter part of 2001, the project encountered serious financial difficulties. The value of Nextel, the mobile telephone company owned by Craig MacCaw, who had for a long time been the largest contributor of funding to the FWKF, fell dramatically on the stock exchange, and MacCaw withdrew his support. The other contributors also began to become impatient, and real results were urgently required.

During the early summer of 2002, Keiko's trips to sea became more frequent and longer. He met wild killer whales on several occasions, but was reticent and there was never any reunion with whales that were probably his relatives. Then, on one of these excursions, Keiko went beyond the range of the VHF tracker and disappeared, until he turned up again in a small fjord on the Møre coast in western Norway on 1 September, after 45 days out on his own.

There, Keiko immediately gained great attention, and people flocked to Skålvik in Halsa to see the celebrity at close quarters. The media presented shots of children rowing close to him and swimming beside him in beautiful, late-summer weather, and Keiko was once more in the limelight.

Keiko's trainers were, however, worried. They saw this as a step backwards for all the efforts that had been put into getting him back to a free life in the sea. Several of them were immediately dispatched to Norway to gain control of the situation.

After the authorities had given assurance that he was safe in Norwegian waters, restrictions were enforced preventing anyone approaching close to Keiko.

Because the sea in Skålvik freezes over in winter, it was decided in the late autumn to move Keiko to nearby Taknesfjord, where he could spend the winter in ice-free surroundings. Gradually, the media lost much of its interest in Keiko, and he no longer attracted many headlines. Not until 12 December 2003, when it was reported that Keiko had died after contracting pneumonia.

Keiko and his trainers at Vestmannaeyer in Iceland.

For the young killer whales, the first years of their lives is a continuous learning process.

It is often controversial to speak of culture in animals, because many people believe this concept should be reserved for human beings. However, if we allow the concept to include 'behaviour and information shared within a population through social learning', it becomes useful in a biological context.

If we imagine two human children growing up, one in a desert environment in Namibia and the other as an Inuit in Greenland, it is obvious that they are growing up under completely different living conditions. They belong to the same species, but are faced with entirely different challenges. They will also learn unrelated languages, and if we allow them to change places after some years they will not immediately feel at home. However, after a while they will learn the new language and behaviour, and thereby adapt to their new environment.

If we then imagine that a young killer whale from the Crozet Islands changes places with one from the Norwegian coast, they would be faced with the same problem. Both would be in an unknown environment with unknown food, without skills in relevant hunting techniques and unable to communicate with fellow members of their species. It is by no means certain that this would have been successful!

Nevertheless, people have recently tried such an experiment. The attempt to bring the celebrity whale, Keiko, back to a life in the open sea as a 'wild' killer whale was precisely such an experiment, but with far poorer odds than in our little hypothesis.

Keiko spent two years with his family off Iceland before he was captured. He was about 26 years old when he was released from a pen and swam freely in the open sea again. We can only guess how much a young killer whale learns during the first two years of its life in the wild, but it is scarcely sufficient to survive on its own.

Keiko's family group, his social network, consisted for most of his life of a group of animal keepers, veterinary surgeons and trainers. They gave him food and taught him a number of tricks and codes that enabled him to tackle his new life. In reality, he spent most of his life learning to become a tame killer whale and socialise with human beings.

Keiko's story was offered a great deal of attention in the media. The project to return him to the wild was surrounded by stubborn optimism on the part of those involved. However, the apparently positive agreement regarding his progress was far from as unanimous as one might get the impression of. The project was controversial right from the start, also among the scientific personnel surrounding Keiko.

If we ignore the ethical aspects of spending millions of dollars to help a single animal, there can scarcely be much disagreement that Keiko had a far better life after he was moved from wretched circumstances in Mexico City to a large sea-water oceanarium in Oregon. However, when he was going to be moved to Iceland, several specialists warned that Keiko lacked the necessary skills to be able to manage on his own. Right up to the time of his death, many people believed Keiko should be returned to the pool in Oregon.

In the team looking after Keiko in Iceland, too, there was disagreement as to whether he would ever be able to survive in the wild, and concern for his health and general fitness. By degrees, the team went a long way towards admitting that Keiko was not an ideal candidate for being returned to the wild. However, after more than ten years' effort and several tens of millions of dollars invested, it was not a viable option to give up. Keiko had to be returned to the sea!

Nowadays, Keiko is often portrayed as an animal which struggled for his right to freedom, made great progress, and finally met death during the final phase of his brave struggle. However, that he had a will of his own seeking freedom is really a quality attributed to him by people wishing to give the project legitimacy; his great progress on the way towards freedom is not scientifically documented.

The two key elements were his ability to acquire food for himself, and the chance of socialising with wild killer whales and obtaining a position in a stable family group.

Keiko met wild killer whales during his excursions to sea from his base in Iceland, but we know little of what really came out of these meetings. In the media, it was assumed that he was together with wild killer whales when he disappeared after a trip in the open sea in 2002, but he turned up alone on the Norwegian coast six weeks later.

Whether Keiko succeeded in feeding himself during the journey is equally uncertain. During all the pandemonium after he appeared in Møre, it was claimed that his long trip from Iceland to Norway was proof that he was now capable of managing on his own and obtaining food on his own accord. However, no proof was ever given that he had eaten. A simple ultrasound scan of his blubber layer would have told us a great deal about his food intake during the month that had passed, but no results of such measurements, or other scientific proof of him having eaten, have been made available.

In fact, most of the evidence suggests that Keiko had not eaten during his long journey, but rather had drained on his fat reserves. When he turned up in a small fjord in Møre on a late summer's day in 2002, he was hungry and longing for company and he did the one thing that could be expected, he sought out people and begged for food.

Even though it was admitted that his renewed contact with people was a setback, and he was fed intensively and given medicines to get him back into shape, stubborn optimism still dominated the team. However, this was playing to the gallery; everyone with a little knowledge of wild killer whales would have understood already then that Keiko would never achieve a life in freedom.

It was obvious that Keiko lacked the fundamental skills to be returned to the wild. When he was caught, he was a mere adolescent who had only just begun to learn what it meant to be a killer whale. After that, he was surrounded by human beings, fed and given medicine. Everything that he should have learnt about communication and hunting techniques was replaced by tricks and begging for food. His original family group is unknown. Everything taken into account, he was an exceptionally poor candidate for the experiment of returning a tame killer whale to freedom in the sea. But he was the world's best known whale, and that was to become his fate.

Keiko was never able to swim into the sunset with the wild killer whales. The NB group in the Vestfjord 2002.

THE FUTURE

— CONSERVATION
OF OUR KILLER WHALES

NATURAL ACCIDENTS

THE KILLER WHALE is on the top of the marine food chain, and has no natural enemies. However, this does not mean it lives a completely risk-free life. There is always a danger that animals may perish in accidents. Occasionally, groups of killer whales strand on a shore, or are confined within fjords by ice or by thresholds at low tide.

The risk of nature-related accidents varies with the environment and the hunting strategy. Killer whales living on sea lions or elephant seals and throwing themselves right up onto the shore to catch their prey naturally run some risk of stranding. Killer whales that hunt seals in Arctic and Antarctic waters may run a risk of freezing into the pack ice.

Such events are rare in Norway, but several groups of killer whales are known to have stranded in the 1860s and 1870s. The only known incident from more recent times was the 14 animals which stranded on a beach in Austnesfjord in Lofoten, on 6 June 1981.

During a spring tide in 1995, four killer whales pursued a herring shoal into a small inlet near Rørvik in Nord-Trøndelag. A few hours later, when the tide ebbed, the whales became trapped. They had no alternative but to wait for the next spring tide, a month later, which would allow them to return to open water. In the meantime, they conserved their energy as much as possible, and spent most of the time resting on the surface. These four whales – NV-1, -2, -4 and -7 – belong to a well-known family group, observed every year in Vestfjord. All of them survived their enforced month of fasting without permanent injury.

In November 1993, a group of five killer whales was surprised by rapidly forming ice in Verrasund, at the head of Trondheimsfjord. A female with her calf, a male and two juveniles had swum into the fjord when a shift in the weather brought severely cold conditions, causing the fjord to freeze. A barrier of ice some 15 km broad formed, but a strong current in the narrowest part of the fjord kept a spacious stretch of open water for the whales to move around in. However, suitable food for killer whales was scarce in the fjord.

After three weeks, an ice breaker tried to open a passage out of the fjord for the whales. The attempt failed, and instead the whales tried to get out of the fjord in their own way. They forced their snouts up through the 15 centimetre thick ice to make breathing holes, and succeeded in progressing about a kilometre down the fjord. However, the following day, only three of the whales were to be seen in the channel; the mother and her calf were never seen again.

The three whales were monitored visually and with hydrophones for the next three weeks.

After 46 days, the temperature rose and the ice had completely thawed and the three whales were able to swim out of the fjord. Just five days later, the fjord froze again, including the channel where the whales had been able to stay alive.

Such nature-related accidents are, however, unusual. They may be fatal for individuals or family groups, but they pose no threat to the population level.

The killer whale is on top of the food chain, but it does not mean that it faces no threats.

The drama in Austnesfjord

On 6 June 1981, the only mass stranding of killer whales we know of in Norway in modern times took place at the small settlement of Laupstad, at the head of Austnesfjord in Lofoten. Sigrund Krane lives there, and she photographed the dramatic events as they unfolded.

– It was my father who told me about the killer whales. He was out setting potatoes, and the whales swam onto the beach close to the potato field. It's not unusual to see killer whales here in the fjord, but he'd never seen anything like this before! So he ran up to the house and asked me to get my new camera. I had to photograph this!

It was a dramatic sight that met Sigrund. 14 whales had swum in and become stranded on the shore. Most of them were adult females, and several had small calves with them. The whales had swum straight on to land. It was high tide, and as the tide went out the creatures were increasingly left high and dry.

– All the villagers soon came to the shore, and quickly agreed to try to get the animals out into the water again. Using big logs, we managed to get the smallest ones out into deeper water, but they immediately swam onto the beach again, clearly to be near their mothers. And as it was impossible to budge the largest animals, the situation seemed critical.

Trond Johansen throws water on one of the stranded killer whales (left), while Arnor Krane (front) and Kjell Krane try to free one of the animals with a pole.

People poured buckets of water over the whales to keep them wet and cool. The animals made lots of noises, and when water was poured over them they moaned with pleasure!

The police had been notified, and came after a while. A fishing boat was fetched to try and tow the whales out into deep water. But disagreement arose as to whether this was the right thing to do, or whether it would be more humane to kill them.

– Some people thought the animals should be killed, but most of the villagers were strongly against this. One reason was that they were afraid the animals would be left lying on the beach to rot, and become a contamination problem. But on the whole, there was a genuine wish to save the magnificent creatures.

The villagers got their way, and with the help of long ropes from the boat and logs used as levers they eventually managed to get all the animals out into the sea again.

– I should think the whole rescue took over three hours, but it was successful in the end. When all the animals were free, they set their course straight out of the fjord and disappeared, says Sigrund Krane.

A local fishing boat was used to drag the largest animals out on deep water.

Individual fates

It is very rare to find dead killer whales in such a state that we can find out something about the cause of their death. This is mainly because a dead killer whale sinks. After a time, the internal development of gas will give the carcass some degree of buoyancy, but it will only reach the surface if it has been lying in comparatively shallow water.

In autumn 2003, a dead killer whale was reported near Risvær in Vestfjord. A search was made for it at the reported position without result, and it was assumed that it had drifted away. However, a few days later, people on a whale safari vessel discovered it floating near Skrova and were able to fasten a rope round its tail and tow it to land. There, scientists and a veterinary surgeon performed an autopsy on it, thus giving us a seldom insight into the fate of an individual whale.

It was a large female, and she died while in labour. Something had gone wrong with the pregnancy, probably at the time of delivery, and the foetus extended part way out of the dead animal. Her stomach was empty, suggesting she had been weak and unable to eat for some time before she died. She had probably found her way into shallow water and died there.

Being all of six metres long, she was a very large female, and judging by the wear on her teeth she was old, probably 40-45 years. This would probably have been her last calf.

Despite her long life, her dorsal fin completely lacked nicks. The saddle patch had been scraped a bit after she had died, but it lacked any distinct marks that coincided with known, identified animals. We are therefore fairly sure she was not one of those we know well.

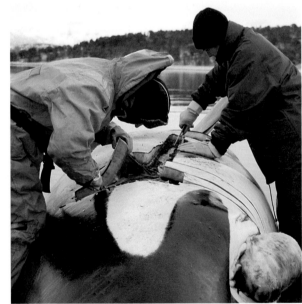

CONFLICTS WITH HUMAN ACTIVITIES

KILLER WHALES LIVE in relatively small populations. There are killer whale populations numbering fewer than one hundred individuals, and which are apparently genetically isolated. The Norwegian herring-feeding population, which is estimated to number some 1000 individuals, is one of the largest killer whale populations we know of.

It is not feasible to consider management on a global level for a species that is dispersed throughout the world in a number of relatively isolated populations. The various killer whale populations are faced with different challenges and threats, and management measures must be accommodated to the individual population. The threats facing a predator at the very top of the food chain are complex and for the most part linked with human activities.

Because killer whales often live on food resources that are also commercially exploited, they have been regarded as competitors, and have therefore been hunted by people. This applies not least in Norway, where they have periodically been hunted quite intensively. From 1938 to 1981, 2435 killer whales were taken during the open

Herring is prey for several birds and animals.

season for small whales in Norwegian waters, more than two hundred being killed some years. Competition for herring was one of the main motives for this hunting, and the collapse of the herring stock was the direct reason for the greatly intensified persecution of killer whales in 1978-81.

Since killer whales have a long life span, live in stable groups and reproduce slowly, the Norwegian hunting has undoubtedly had a considerable impact on the population. However, all hunting of killer whales ceased in 1981.

We know much more about Norwegian killer whales now than we did 25 years ago.

We know the population feeding on herring is unable to increase rapidly in numbers due to its slow reproductive rate. The tagging in 2000 and 2001 showed that these whales travel further afield than we assumed. It therefore seems likely that the size of the population has been over-estimated in the past. The amount of herring consumed by the whales is modest considering the size of the Norwegian spring-spawning herring stock, and there is no reason to consider them as a serious competitor for this stock.

The live capture of killer whales for aquariums became a threat for some populations in the second half of last century. Off British Columbia it took place on such a large scale that it clearly had an effect on the populations, and it continued off Iceland up to 1988 – long after the killer whales were internationally protected. Today, this practice has largely ceased, but both Japan and Russia have permitted it until very recently. Killer whales have not been captured for aquariums in Norwegian waters.

In Norway, there is a potential danger that the main prey of killer whales disappears as a consequence of over-fishing. We

Some killer whales, like the male NO-10, lack the tip of the dorsal fin. Such injuries are probably caused by boat propellers.

have already on one occasion reduced the Norwegian spring-spawning herring stock close to extinction. Can we succeed in maintaining the stock at a sufficiently high level to enable it to be a basis for one of our largest fisheries and at the same time provide food for killer whales and many other species in the marine ecosystem?

We know little about the effect which the collapse in the Norwegian spring-spawning herring stock had on the killer whales in the 1960s and 1970s. It may have been considerably more difficult for them to find food, and they may have begun pursuing alternative, less optimal prey species. It is likely that they spent more time and energy obtaining enough food, and the result may have been reduced fat reserves and poorer fitness. This normally causes lower resistance to disease, and reduced reproduction.

Whereas several other species of whales regularly become entangled in nets and die, fishing gear does not seem to pose a lethal threat to killer whales. However, there are a few reports of killer whales which have drowned in herring nets; in most cases, the drowned animals have been very young – adult whales can cut their way out of the net, Contact with fishing gear may well explain many of the notches and cuts we observe on dorsal fins of killer whales. The material which the strong herring net is made of can cut into the dorsal fin of killer whales swimming through the nets.

Killer whales with large cuts and notches in the top of their dorsal fin have probably been in contact with boat propellers. They apparently have the ability to navigate with high precision, but do not seem to be always capable of estimating the distance between the top of their dorsal fin and, for example, a boat propeller. However, the dorsal fin is mainly made of cartilage and has relatively few nerves. The cuts and notches therefore seem to be mainly "cosmetic" injuries – the Norwegian identification catalogue contains images of individuals with more than 1/3 of the dorsal fin lost, and these animals seem to thrive as well as others in the family groups.

The fisheries also result in a great deal of traffic on the sea and it would seem likely that the killer whales, which to a large extent communicate acoustically, would be disturbed by engine noise. However, the large numbers of herring boats in Nordland fjords in late autumn do not seem to affect the killer whales. On the contrary, the whales actually follow the fishing fleet, since they get easy meals from herring which escape from the nets.

The use of echo sounders by the fishing boats does not seem to bother the killer whales, either. However, during a naval exercise in Vestfjord in 2000, when powerful sonars were used to search for submarines, killer whales were not observed in the area for the duration of the exercise.

Smaller, faster boats seem to have more effect on killer whale behaviour than larger, slower vessels. This is probably related to the higher frequency of the noise created by outboard engines than other engines. Whale-watching boats which continuously change speed and direction are also stressful for the whales.

As interest for the killer whales has grown, whale-watching has become a lucrative business. We are faced with a great challenge here. Our well-meaning love of these beautiful and impressive animals may also be a threat to them!

In Victoria Sound, on the border between the USA and Canada, the killer whales are concentrated in protected fjords where conditions are ideal for whale-watching. More than six million people reside in the surrounding cities of Seattle, Vancouver and Victoria, and these, together with many summer visitors, offer an almost inexhaustible market for this business, which has grown at record speed during the last few decades. There are now more than 70 commercial safari boats, many of them going out several times a day, in addition to countless private boats. All this traffic will obviously be a great burden on a killer whale population numbering fewer than one hundred.

Here in Norway, we are faced with some of the same challenges in the fjords of northern Nordland. More and more people want to go out to see killer whales at close range, and in recent years there has been a particularly rapid growth in whale-watching trips using small, fast boats and offering the chance to swim with the killer whales. We want to get closer and closer, preferably in the water with the whales, and we have less and less time. This can easily lead to foolish, aggressive boat handling which stresses the animals.

In the mid-1990s, the operators of the Norwegian whale safari market became aware of this problem, and they and the scientists joined forces to draw up a code of conduct for killer whale watching in

Killer whales react very differently to fast, small boats and larger vessels.

The young killer whale called "Anna" is known to be very curious towards the whale safari vessels. She comes up and says "hello" when whistled to

The truly great whale safari adventure always happens when the safari-boat is laying still.

A young killer whale tries to bite the rudder of the safari vessel.

Tysfjord and inner Vestfjord. This was adhered to, and for a number of years consideration for the animals formed the basis for the entire whale watching activity in the area. However, recently the number of operators has risen dramatically. Competition has entered into the whale safari market, and it is no longer as easy to gather all the operators behind a common set of rules. In addition, an increasing number of people in private boats want to go out and experience the killer whales. Even though this activity is on a different scale from that in Victoria Sound, the situation in Tysfjord on a fine November weekend may seem quite chaotic.

This is a growing problem that does not seem to have an immediate and simple solution. It is neither desirable nor possible to introduce restrictions on traffic in these fjords in the middle of a fishing season, and such restrictions would be extremely difficult to enforce. Information and appeals to show consideration are the proper way to approach this problem.

Everyone who has been killer whale watching knows that the greatest thrills are experienced when the boat is able to stand still and the whales can themselves choose to approach it. When the whales have just eaten and are playful they often

approach stationary boats. One should never approach resting whales or pursue a group of whales which is clearly avoiding the boat.

It is vital to understand killer whale behaviour when one intends to allow people to enter the water and swim with killer whales. It is extremely important that the whales are allowed to approach the boat, rather than the boat pursuing them. An underwater encounter with a killer whale generally lasts only a few seconds, but it takes place at close quarters and is a memory of a lifetime for those who experience it. However, people who want to swim with the whales run the risk of staying in the boat the whole day without even getting into the water, because there is no means of making contact with a killer whale which does not itself choose to swim close by you!

Many people are preoccupied with whether it is safe to venture into the water with killer whales. After all, they hunt large mammals elsewhere in the world, occasionally in our waters, too. It is obviously impossible to give any form of guarantee in connection with activities that entail close contact with wild animals. Nevertheless, wild killer whales have never attacked human beings.

To get a close encounter with killer whales under water, divers are totally dependent of the whales choosing to come near them.

POLLUTION

ANOTHER THREAT TO the killer whales caused by humans is pollution. For more than half a century, we have been producing environmental pollutants, and many of them have found their way into the oceans. Several of these are substances that do not break down, but accumulate up through the food chain. They are taken up by plankton, which in turn are eaten by fish, which may be eaten by larger fish that are consumed by marine mammals. As neither the fish nor the mammals are able to rid themselves of these pollutants, the concentration of the toxic chemicals increases through each link in the chain.

It is reasonable to assume that measurable levels of several pollutants will be found in the blubber or liver of a killer whale anywhere in the world. Their level increases throughout the life of the killer whale. Many of them are soluble in fat, which means that males accumulate environmental pollutants in their fatty tissue all their lives. The females also accumulate them, but may get rid of some of the toxic load when they nurse their calves. They will then pass the pollutants on to their offspring through their extremely fatty milk.

We know little about how the environmental pollutants act as long as they are stored in the fatty tissue. Nor is it a question of individual substances; a combination of several substances is usually found when samples from marine mammals are analysed, and we have little knowledge of how these various substances affect one another. However, laboratory trials have shown that many hinder reproduction and cause a reduced immune response in animals.

Another threat is petroleum production. The plans for further oil and gas production in the Norwegian Sea, including the Lofoten area, and in the Barents Sea, and the ever-increasing volumes being transported along the coast of northern Norway, increase the risk of spills.

We know a good deal about the effect of oil pollution on killer whales in the wake of the Exxon Valdez disaster in Alaska in March 1989. One of the large fish-feeding groups – the AB group – was close to the site at the time. This group, which originally numbered 36 individuals, was observed swimming in the oil slick only four days after the accident. Seven whales, three old females and four juveniles, were already missing, and were never seen again. The following spring, a further six whales were missing, and three calves which had lost their mothers vanished during the succeeding years. Even though new calves are being born into the AB group, it has still not regained its previous size, whereas all the other family groups in this population have grown in numbers during this period.

We do not know for certain how the oil affects killer whales, but it seems probable that inhaling the petroleum gases damages the lungs and respiratory passages, and that such damage may be critical for a whale.

A group of mammal-feeding killer whales – AT1 – was probably also affected by the Exxon Valdez disaster. Because these whales do not keep together in stable family groups like fish-feeding whales do, we know less about the development of the AT1 group, but 9 of the 22 members disappeared in the years following the disaster. Some were observed close to the Exxon Valdez immediately after it foundered. Mammal-feeding killer whales are probably still more prone to oil pollution because they may eat soiled prey and hence take up oil in that way.

The female killer whales will pass the pollutants on to their offspring through the milk.

THE FUTURE

AS THE NEW MILLENNIUM dawns, the Norwegian killer whale population seems to be viable. However, small changes in the environment and living conditions may have great consequences for these charismatic creatures. A great deal depends on us and ultimately it largely boils down to national and international environmental policies and resource management.

Will the killer whales have enough food in the future? This depends on whether we succeed in maintaining the herring stock at a viable level. It is strong today, and the older herring enter the fjords to spend the winter. There, every kind of vessel is allowed to fish – from the smallest one-man boat to seiners several hundred feet long – and incredible quantities of herring are caught. Can the herring stock tolerate this pressure? Are we taking enough precautions and ensuring a sustainable level of fishing? Or will we yet again fish the herring to such an extent that the stock collapses, with major consequences for other species of fish, seabirds and killer whales?

Will drilling for oil and gas begin in our biologically most productive waters? Can we ensure that the ever-increasing transport of oil along the coast of North Norway takes place safely? A major oil spill here is a nightmare scenario few can bear to imagine. It would have enormous consequences for the ecosystem, and hit both the fisheries and the bird and animal life. The consequences for the killer whale population could be dramatic.

What will we learn from the samples of environmental pollutants taken from killer whales? If they contain such large concentrations as we have reason to fear, where do these toxins originate and how are the killer whales acquiring them? As Norwegian killer whales live almost exclusively on herring, the answer is decidedly unpleasant for more than the killer whales, because the poisons are necessarily accumulating through the herring.

All these are factors about which we know little and which concern the balance of the entire marine ecosystem. However, as we learn more about the killer whale, it will be able to tell us more about the ecosystem. Continuing targeted research into killer whales will be an important contribution towards monitoring the state of health of our northern waters.

Hopefully future generations can also experience the big killer whale bull breaking the surface in Tysfjord, with the spectacular Mount Stetnd in the background.

PHOTOGRAPHERS

John Stenersen: front cover, p. 9, 10, 11, 12, 13, 14-15, 19, 21, 22-23, 26-27, 32, 37, 41, 43, 46, 47, 49, 54, 56, 57, 61, 65, 66, 67, 69, 72, 75, 78, 83, 84, 86, 87, 89, 91, 93, back cover.

Tiu Similä: p. 4, 5, 33, 38, 39, 48, 51, 59, 71.

George McCallum: p. 20, 44, 50, 82, 88.

Mic Calvert: p. 34, 35.

Fernando Ugarte: p. 52 (video clips).

Sigrund Krane: p. 80, 81 (v).

Politiet i Svolvær: p. 81 (h).

Juha Taskinen: p. 95

An overwiev of recent killer whale research from different parts of the world, can be found in the summary from the Fourth International Orca Symposium and Workshop, September 23-28 2002. CEBC-CNR, France.

The documents can be found on internett at: www.cebc.cnrs.fr

JOHN STENERSEN – born in Oslo 1957.

He is a photographer with background from press and art photography. In 1995 he moved to the Lofoten Islands, and has since that mainly worked with nature photography.
He is a dedicated ornithologist, and has experience as a field-worker with research on bird migration and seabird monitoring. He has written several popular scientific articles, and made a book about the birds of the Lofoten Islands in 1995.
He also works as a nature-guide in Lofoten, and as guide on killer whale safaris in Tysfjord.

TIU SIMILÄ – born in Helsingfors 1960.

She completed her MSc degree in hydrobiology at the University of Helsinki in 1989.
In 1986 she participated in a research project on killer whales in northern Norway and since 1987 she has been leading this project with support from WWF.
In 1997 she completed her PhD thesis at the University of Tromsø on behavioural biology of killer whales. Her main research interest is in interactions between killer whales and herring and she has participated in the satellite tracking project on Norwegian killer whales.

Literature

Baird, R.W. 2002. Killer Whales of the world. Natural History and Conservation. Voyageur Press Inc.

Bisther, A., Vongraven,D. 2001. Killer whales feeding on both marine mammals and fish: A transient, resident or opportunistic type. Poster presentation, 14th Biennial Conference on the Biology of Marine Mammals, Vancouver, British Columbia, Canada 28 Nov-3 Dec 2001.

Christensen, I. 1982. Killer whales in Norwegian coastal waters. Rep.In. Whaling Comm 32: 633-672.

Christensen, I. 1984. Growth and reproduction of killer whales, Orcinus orca, in Norwegian coastal waters. Rep. int. Whal. Commn /special issue 6):253-258.

Damsgård, B. Houg, C. (editors). 2000. Spekkhogger - staurkval. Ottar. Populærvitenskapelig tidskrift for Tromsø Museum. Nr. 230.

Domenici, P., Batty, R.S., Similä, T. and Ogam, E. 2000. Killer whales (Orcinus orca) feeding on schooling herring (Clupea harengus) using underwater tailslaps: kinematic analyses of field observations. The Journal of Experimental Biology, 203: 283-294.

Ford, J.K.B., Ellis, G.M. 1999. Transients: Mammal-Hunting Killer whales of British Columbia, Washington and Southeastern Alaska. University of Washington Press.

Ford, J.K.B., Ellis, G.E., and Balcomb, K.C. 2000. Killer Whales, second edition. UBC Press.

Hoyt, E. 1990. Orca. The Whale Called Killer. Camden House.

Jonsgård, Å. 1968. A note on the attacking behaviour of the killer whales (Orcinus orca). Nor. Hvalfangs-Tid. 57: 84-85.

Jonsgård, Å, Lyshoel, P.B. 1970. A contribution to the knowledge of the biology of the killer whale Orcinus orca (L.). Nytt. Mag. Zool.(Oslo). 18: 41-48.

Juul-Simon, M. 2004. Sounds produced by foraging killer whales (Orcinus orca). Msc thesis. Institute of Biology, The University of Southern Denmark – Odense.

Sigurjonsson, J., Leatherwood, S. (editors). 1988. North Atlantic killer whales. Rit Fiskideildar, Vol XI. Journal of the Marine Research Institute, Reykjavik.

Similä, T.1997. Sonar observations of killer whales (Orcinus orca) feeding on herring schools. Aquatic Mammals 23 (3): 119-126.

Similä, T. 1997. Behavioural ecology of killer whales in northern Norway. PhD thesis, University of Tromsø.

Similä, T. and Ugarte, F. 1993. Surface and underwater observations of cooperatively feeding killer whales. Can. J.Zool.71:1494-1499.

Similä, T., Holst, J.C., and Christensen, I. 1996. Patterns in seasonal occurrence and diet of killer whales in northern Norway with reference to the distribution and abundance of Norwegian spring-spawning herring. Can.J.Fish.Aquat.Sci. 1996:53:769-779.

Strager, H. 1995. Pod-specific call repertoires and compound calls of killer whales, Orcinus orca, in the waters of northen Norway. Can. J. Zool. 73: 1037-1047.

Ugarte, F. Behaviour and social organisation of killer whales in Northern Norway. MSc thesis, Norwegian College of Fisheries Science. University of Tromsø 2001.